Working Papers, Volume 1
Chapters 1-12

for use with

Fundamental Accounting Principles

Eighteenth Edition

John J. Wild
University of Wisconsin, Madison

Kermit D. Larson
University of Texas at Austin

Barbara Chiappetta
Nassau Community College

Prepared by
John J. Wild
University of Wisconsin, Madison

Boston   Burr Ridge, IL   Dubuque, IA   Madison, WI   New York   San Francisco   St. Louis
Bangkok   Bogotá   Caracas   Kuala Lumpur   Lisbon   London   Madrid   Mexico City
Milan   Montreal   New Delhi   Santiago   Seoul   Singapore   Sydney   Taipei   Toronto

Working Papers, Volume 1, Chapters 1-12 for use with
FUNDAMENTAL ACCOUNTING PRINCIPLES
John J. Wild, Kermit D. Larson, and Barbara Chiappetta

Published by McGraw-Hill, an imprint of The McGraw-Hill Companies, Inc., 1221 Avenue of the Americas,
New York, NY 10020. Copyright © 2007 by The McGraw-Hill Companies, Inc. All rights reserved.

1 2 3 4 5 6 7 8 9 0 CUS/CUS 0 9 8 7 6 5

ISBN: 978-0-07-332522-4
MHID: 0-07-332522-8

Table of Contents

Name _____

(a)

GAAP:
Importance: _____
_____
_____
_____

SEC:
Importance: _____
_____
_____
_____
_____
_____

FASB:
Importance: _____
_____
_____

IASB
Importance: _____
_____
_____
_____
_____

Quick Study 1-2

(a)	_____	(g)	_____
(b)	_____	(h)	_____
(c)	_____	(i)	_____
(d)	_____	(j)	_____
(e)	_____	(k)	_____
(f)	_____	(l)	_____

Quick Study 1-3

_____
_____
_____
_____

(1) _____

_____

_____

(2) _____

_____

_____

_____

(3) _____

_____

_____

(4) _____

_____

_____

Quick Study 1-5

_____

_____

_____

_____

_____

Quick Study 1-6

(a) _____

(b) _____

(c) _____

Quick Study 1-7

	Assets	=	Liabilities	+	Equity
(a)					
(b)					

Quick Study 1-8

	Assets	=	Liabilities	+	Equity
	$ 75,000		(a) _____		$40,000
(b) _____			$25,000		$70,000
	$ 85,000		$20,000		(c) _____

Name _____

Business transactions:

_____
_____
_____

Business events:

_____
_____
_____
_____

Quick Study 1-10

(a) (1) _____
    (2) _____
    (3) _____

(b)	Assets	=	Liabilities	+	Equity
		=		+	

Quick Study 1-11

(a) _____ (d) _____ (g) _____
(b) _____ (e) _____ (h) _____
(c) _____ (f) _____ (i) _____

Quick Study 1-12

Return on Assets:

_____
_____
_____

Interpretation:

_____
_____
_____

(1) _____
(2) _____
(3) _____
(4) _____
(5) _____
(6) _____
(7) _____
(8) _____

Exercise 1-2

External User:	_____
	_____
	_____
	_____
External User:	_____
	_____
	_____
	_____
External User:	_____
	_____
	_____
	_____

Exercise 1-3

(a) _____
_____
_____
_____

(b) _____
_____
_____
_____

(c) _____
_____
_____
_____

(d) _____
_____
_____
_____

Chapter 1   Exercise 1-4

Name _____

(a) _____

(b) _____

(c) _____

(d) _____

(e) _____

(f) _____

(g) _____

Exercise 1-5

(1) _____

(2) _____

(3) _____

(4) _____

(5) _____

(6) _____

(7) _____

Exercise 1-6

(1) _____

(2) _____

(3) _____

(4) _____

(5) _____

Name _____

	Assets	=	Liabilities	+	Equity
(a)					
(b)					
(c)					

Exercise 1-8

(a) _____

(b) _____

(c) _____

(d) _____

(e) _____

(f) _____

(g) _____

(a) _____

_____

(b) _____

_____

(c) _____

_____

(d) _____

_____

(e) _____

_____

Exercise 1-10

(a) _____

_____

_____

(b) _____

_____

_____

_____

_____

(c) _____

_____

_____

_____

_____

Name _____

	Assets			Liabilities		Equity			
Cash	+ Accounts Receivable	+ Equipment =		Accounts Payable	+	Holden, Capital -	Holden, Withdrawals	+ Revenues	- Expenses
(a)									
(b)									
(c)									
(d)									
(e)									
(f)									
(g)									
(h)									
(i)									
(j)									

Exercise 1-12

(a) _____

_____

(b) _____

_____

(c) _____

_____

(d) _____

_____

(e) _____

_____

Income Statement

Exercise 1-14

Exercise 1-16

    Name _____

(1) _____   (5) _____
(2) _____   (6) _____
(3) _____   (7) _____
(4) _____   (8) _____

Exercise 1-18

 Return on Assets: _____

_____

_____

Interpretation: _____

_____

Exercise 1-19^B

(a) _____
(b) _____
(c) _____
(d) _____
(e) _____

Part 1: Company_____

(a) _____

_____

_____

_____

_____

(b) _____

_____

_____

_____

_____

_____

_____

(c) _____

_____

_____

_____

_____

Part 2: Company_____

(a) _____

_____

_____

(b) _____

_____

(c) _____

_____

_____

_____

_____

Part 3: Company_____

_____

_____

_____

_____

_____

_____

_____

_____

_____

_____

_____

_____

_____

_____

_____

_____

_____

_____

Chapter 1   Problem 1-1A or 1-1B
           (Continued)
                              Name _____

Part 4: Company_____

_____
_____
_____
_____
_____
_____
_____
_____
_____
_____
_____
_____
_____
_____
_____
_____

Part 5: Company_____

_____
_____
_____
_____
_____
_____
_____
_____
_____
_____
_____
_____
_____
_____
_____
_____
_____

Name _____

TRANSACTION	Balance Sheet			INCOME Stmt.	Statement of Cash Flows		
	TOTAL ASSETS	TOTAL LIABILITIES	TOTAL EQUITY	NET INCOME	OPERATING ACTIVITIES	FINANCING ACTIVITIES	INVESTING ACTIVITIES
1.							
2.							
3.							
4.							
5.							
6.							
7.							
8.							
9.							
10.							

Income Statement

Problem 1-4A or 1-4B

Balance Sheet

Problem 1-5A or 1-5B

Statement of Cash Flows

Statement of Owner's Equity

Name _____

DATE	ASSETS			=	LIABILITIES +	EQUITY				
	CASH +	ACCOUNTS + RECEIVABLE	EQUIPMENT	=	ACCOUNTS PAYABLE	Capital	- Withdrawals	+ REVENUES	- EXPENSES

Income Statement

Statement of Owner's Equity

Balance Sheet

Statement of Cash Flows

Parts 1 and 2

Name _____

DATE	ASSETS				= LIABILITIES	EQUITY			
	CASH	+ ACCOUNTS RECEIVABLE	+ OFFICE SUPPLIES	+ OFFICE EQUIPMENT	= ACCOUNTS PAYABLE +	Capital	– Withdrawals	+ REVENUES	– EXPENSES

Income Statement

Statement of Owner's Equity

Balance Sheet

Statement of Cash Flows

Part 4

Name _____

	ASSETS					LIABILITIES		EQUITY			
	CASH +	ACCOUNTS + RECEIVABLE	OFFICE + SUPPLIES	OFFICE + EQUIPMENT	BUILDING =	ACCOUNTS + PAYABLE	NOTES + PAYABLE	Capital	– Withdrawals	+ REVENUES	– EXPENSES
a.											
b.											
Bal.											
c.											
Bal.											
d.											
Bal.											
e.											
Bal.											
f.											
Bal.											
g.											
Bal.											
h.											
Bal.											
i.											
Bal.											
j.											
Bal.											
k.											
Bal.											

_____

_____

_____

Problem 1-10A or 1-10B

(1a) _____

_____

(1b) _____

_____

(2) _____

_____

_____

(3) _____

_____

_____

(4) _____

_____

_____

_____

_____

_____

_____

(1) _____

_____

_____

(2) _____

_____

_____

(3) _____

_____

_____

(4) _____

_____

_____

Problem 1-12A or 1-12B

(1) Return: _____

_____

Risk: _____

_____

(2) Return: _____

_____

Risk: _____

_____

(3) Return: _____

_____

Risk: _____

_____

(4) Return: _____

_____

Risk: _____

_____

_____

(1) _____   (5) _____
(2) _____   (6) _____
(3) _____   (7) _____
(4) _____   (8) _____

Problem 1-14A

(1) Major Activity: _____
_____
_____

(2) Major Activity: _____
_____
_____

(3) Major Activity: _____
_____
_____

Problem 1-14B

I: _____
  A. _____
  B. _____

II. _____
  A. _____
  B. _____

III. _____
  A. _____
  B. _____

Chapter 1   Serial Problem-SP 1   Success Systems   Name _____

		ASSETS				LIABILITIES	EQUITY			
DATE	CASH +	ACCOUNTS + RECEIVABLE	COMPUTER + SUPPLIES	COMPUTER + EQUIPMENT	OFFICE EQUIPMENT	= ACCOUNTS + PAYABLE	A. Lopez, Capital	A. Lopez, - Withdrawals	+ REVENUES	- EXPENSES
Oct. 1										
3										
Bal.										
6										
Bal.										
8										
Bal.										
12										
Bal.										
15										
Bal.										
17										
Bal.										
20										
Bal.										
22										
Bal.										
28										
Bal.										
31										
Bal.										
31										
Bal.										

Name _____

(1) _____
_____
_____

(2) _____
_____
_____

(3) _____
_____
_____

(4) _____
_____
_____
_____

(5) **Fast Forward:** _____
_____
_____
_____

Chapter 1 Comparative Analysis--BTN 1-2 *Name* ______________________

Best Buy	Circuit City
(1)	
(2)	
(3)	

(4)

(5)

Ethics Challenge--BTN 1-3

(1)

(2)

(3)

(4)

Name _____

(1)   *--Request For Information--*

(2) _____

1. _____
_____
_____
_____
_____
_____
_____

2. _____
_____
_____
_____

Teamwork in Action--BTN 1-6

(1) **Meeting Time and Place:** _____
_____

(2) **Telephone and E-mail Addresses:** _____
_____
_____
_____
_____
_____

Instructor Notification: [ ]   **YES** _____

Chapter 1 *BusinessWeek* Activity   Name _____
          BTN 1-7

(1)   1 _____
       2 _____
       3 _____
       4 _____
       5 _____
       6 _____
       7 _____
       8 _____
       9 _____
      10 _____
(2)   1 _____
       2 _____
       3 _____
       4 _____
       5 _____
       6 _____
       7 _____
       8 _____
       9 _____
      10 _____
(3) _____
_____
_____
_____

Entrepreneurial Decision--BTN 1-8
(1)(a) _____
_____
_____
_____
_____

  (b) _____
_____
_____
_____

(2) _____
_____
_____
_____
_____
_____
_____

Name _____

(1) _____
_____
_____
_____
_____
_____

(2) _____
_____
_____
_____
_____
_____

(3) _____
_____
_____
_____
_____
_____

Global Decision--BTN 1-10

(1) _____
_____
_____
_____
_____
_____

(2) _____
_____
_____
_____
_____
_____

Likely source documents are:

_____
_____
_____
_____
_____

Quick Study 2-2

(a) _____		(f) _____	
(b) _____		(g) _____	
(c) _____		(h) _____	
(d) _____		(i) _____	
(e) _____			

Quick Study 2-3

(a) _____		(g) _____	
(b) _____		(h) _____	
(c) _____		(i) _____	
(d) _____		(j) _____	
(e) _____		(k) _____	
(f) _____		(l) _____	

Quick Study 2-4

(a) _____		(f) _____	
(b) _____		(g) _____	
(c) _____		(h) _____	
(d) _____		(i) _____	
(e) _____		(j) _____	

Quick Study 2-5

(a) _____		(e) _____	
(b) _____		(f) _____	
(c) _____		(g) _____	
(d) _____		(h) _____	
		(i) _____	

GENERAL JOURNAL

Date		Account Titles and Explanation	P.R.	Debit	Credit

Quick Study 2-7

_____

_____

_____

_____

_____

Quick Study 2-8

(a) _____   (f) _____

(b) _____   (g) _____

(c) _____   (h) _____

(d) _____   (i) _____

(e) _____   (j) _____

Name _____

ACCOUNT	TYPE OF ACCOUNT	INCREASE (Dr. or Cr.)	NORMAL BALANCE
a.			
b.			
c.			
d.			
e.			
f.			
g.			
h.			
i.			
j.			
k.			
l.			

Exercise 2-2

(a) _____

_____

_____

_____

_____

_____

_____

_____

(b) _____

_____

_____

_____

_____

_____

_____

(c) _____

_____

_____

_____

_____

_____

_____

_____

GENERAL JOURNAL

Date	Account Titles and Explanation	P.R.	Debit	Credit

Name _____

Cash	Photography Equipment

M. Harris, Capital

Photography Fees Earned

Office Supplies	Utilities Expense

Prepaid Insurance

Trial Balance

Assets Liabilities   Cap.   W   R   E
  1   2   3   4   5   6

Chapter 2   Exercise 2-6   Name Amena Company

Cash	
a) 13,325	b) 475
d) 2,000	e) 6235
h) 2300	g) 775
	i) 800
9340	

Accounts Payable	
e) 6235	c) 6235
	0

A. Amena, Capital	
	a) 13,325

Accounts Receivable	
f) 3,300	h) 2300
1000	

A. Amena, Withdrawals	
i) 800	

Office Supplies	
b) 475	
475	

Fees Earned	
	d) 2000
	f) 3300
	5300

Office Equipment	
c) 6235	
6235	

Rent Expense	
g) 775	

Exercise 2-7

Amena Company
Trial Balance
5/31/08

Cash	9340	
Acc Rec	1000	
Off Sup	475	
Office Equip	6235	
A/A Cap		13,325
A/A W/D	800	
Fees Earned		5300
Rent	775	
	18,625	18,625

Right margin notes:

a) + 13,325 (Ass) cash
+ 13,325 (OE) AA Cap

b) - 475 cash
+ 475 Off. S.
(Both Assets)

c) + 6235 A/P (Liab)
+ 6235 Off E (Assets)

d) + 2000 cash (Asset)
+ 2,000 (Fees Earn)

e) - 6235 (cash (Asset)
- 6235 A/P (Liab)

f) + 3300 A/R
+ 3300 Fees Earn (OE Rev)

g) - 775 cash (Assets)
+ 775 Rent (X-OE)

h) + 2,300 cash (Asset)
= 2,300 A/R

i) - 800 cash
+ 800 OW

GENERAL JOURNAL

Date		Account Titles and Explanation	P.R.	Debit	Credit

Transactions not creating revenues and the reasons: _____

_____

_____

_____

_____

_____

_____

_____

_____

_____

_____

_____

_____

_____

_____

_____

_____

GENERAL JOURNAL

Date		Account Titles and Explanation	P.R.	Debit	Credit

Transactions not creating expenses and the reasons: _____

_____

_____

_____

_____

_____

_____

_____

_____

_____

_____

_____

_____

_____

_____

_____

_____

Income Statement

Exercise 2-11

Statement of Owner's Equity

Name _____

Balance Sheet

(a) Net Income (Loss) = [   ]
     Supporting Computations: _____

_____

_____

_____

_____

_____

_____

_____

_____

(b) Net Income (Loss) = [   ]
     Supporting Computations: _____

_____

_____

_____

_____

_____

_____

_____

_____

_____

(c) Net Income (Loss) = [   ]
     Supporting Computations: _____

_____

_____

_____

_____

_____

_____

_____

_____

(d) Net Income (Loss) = [   ]
     Supporting Computations: _____

_____

_____

_____

_____

_____

_____

_____

_____

Name _____

	(a)	(b)	(c)	(d)

Exercise 2-15

(a) _____

(b) _____

(c) _____

(d) _____

(e) _____

(f) _____

(g) _____

GENERAL JOURNAL

Date	Account Titles and Explanation	P.R.	Debit	Credit
(a)				
(b)				
(c)				
(d)				
(e)				
(f)				
(g)				

	Description	(1) Difference between Debit and Credit Columns	(2) Column with the Larger Total	(3) Identify account(s) incorrectly stated	(4) Amount that account(s) is overstated or understated
(a)	$3,600 debit to Rent Expense is posted as a $1,340 debit.	$2,260	Credit	Rent Expense	Rent Expense is understated by $2,260
(b)					
(c)					
(d)					
(e)					
(f)					
(g)					

(a) _____

_____

_____

_____

(b) _____

_____

_____

(c) _____

_____

_____

(d) _____

_____

_____

(e) _____

_____

_____

_____

Name _____

Part a

(1) _____

(2) _____

(3) _____

(4) _____

(5) _____

(6) _____

_____

Part b

_____

_____

_____

Part c

_____

_____

_____

_____

Part d

_____

_____

_____

Part e

_____

_____

Part f

_____

_____

_____

Name _____

GENERAL JOURNAL

Date	Account Titles and Explanation	P.R.	Debit	Credit
	A) Cash		65,000	
	Office Equip		5,750	
	Computer		30,000	
	Orethus Capital			100,750
	B) Land		22,000	
	Cash			5,000
	Note Payable			17,000
	C) Building		34,500	
	Cash			34,500
	D) Prepaid Ins		5,000	
	Cash			5,000
	E) Cash		4,600	
	Service Reven.			4,600
	F) Computer Equipt.		4,500	
	Cash			8,000
	Note Payable			3,700
	G) Accts Receivable		4,250	
	Fees Earned			4,250
	H) Office Equip		950	
	Accts Payable			950
	I) Acct Receivable		10,200	
	Fees Earned			10,200
	J) Computer Rental Exp		580	
	Account Payable			580
	K) Cash		5,100	
	Acct Receivable			5,100
	L) Wage Exp		1,800	
	Cash			1,800
	M) Accts Payable		950	
	Cash			950
	N) Repairs Expense		608	
	Cash			608
	O) D.G. W/D		6230	
	Cash			6230
	P) Wages Exp		1800	
	Cash			1800
	Q) Adv. Exp		750	
	Cash			750

Name _____

GENERAL JOURNAL

Date	Account Titles and Explanation	P.R.	Debit	Credit

Part 2

Cash   **No. 101**

DATE	PR	Debit	Credit	Balance

Accounts Payable   **No. 201**

DATE	PR	Debit	Credit	Balance

Notes Payable   **No. 250**

DATE	PR	Debit	Credit	Balance

_____, Capital   **No. 301**

DATE	PR	Debit	Credit	Balance

Accounts Receivable   **No. 106**

DATE	PR	Debit	Credit	Balance

_____, Withdrawals   **No. 302**

DATE	PR	Debit	Credit	Balance

Prepaid Insurance   **No. 108**

DATE	PR	Debit	Credit	Balance

Fees Earned   **No. 402**

DATE	PR	Debit	Credit	Balance

Office Equipment   **No. 163**

DATE	PR	Debit	Credit	Balance

Wages Expense   **No. 601**

DATE	PR	Debit	Credit	Balance

_____ Equipment   **No. 164**

DATE	PR	Debit	Credit	Balance

_____ Rental Expense **No. 602**

DATE	PR	Debit	Credit	Balance

Building   **No. 170**

DATE	PR	Debit	Credit	Balance

Advertising Expense   **No. 603**

DATE	PR	Debit	Credit	Balance

Land   **No. 172**

DATE	PR	Debit	Credit	Balance

Repairs Expense   **No. 604**

DATE	PR	Debit	Credit	Balance

Trial Balance

Name _____

GENERAL JOURNAL

Date	Account Titles and Explanation	P.R.	Debit	Credit

Date	Account Titles and Explanation	P.R.	Debit	Credit

GENERAL LEDGER

Cash   ACCOUNT NO. 101

Date	Explanation	P.R.	DEBIT	CREDIT	BALANCE

Accounts Receivable   ACCOUNT NO. 106

Date	Explanation	P.R.	DEBIT	CREDIT	BALANCE

Office Supplies   ACCOUNT NO. 124

Date	Explanation	P.R.	DEBIT	CREDIT	BALANCE

Prepaid Insurance   ACCOUNT NO. 128

Date	Explanation	P.R.	DEBIT	CREDIT	BALANCE

Prepaid Rent   ACCOUNT NO. 131

Date	Explanation	P.R.	DEBIT	CREDIT	BALANCE

Office Equipment   ACCOUNT NO. 163

Date	Explanation	P.R.	DEBIT	CREDIT	BALANCE

Accounts Payable   ACCOUNT NO. 201

Date	Explanation	P.R.	DEBIT	CREDIT	BALANCE

_____, Capital   ACCOUNT NO. 301

Date	Explanation	P.R.	DEBIT	CREDIT	BALANCE

_____, Withdrawals   ACCOUNT NO. 302

Date	Explanation	P.R.	DEBIT	CREDIT	BALANCE

Services Revenue   ACCOUNT NO. 403

Date	Explanation	P.R.	DEBIT	CREDIT	BALANCE

Utilities Expense   ACCOUNT NO. 690

Date	Explanation	P.R.	DEBIT	CREDIT	BALANCE

Part 3

Trial Balance

GENERAL JOURNAL

Date	Account Titles and Explanation	P.R.	Debit	Credit

Date	Account Titles and Explanation	P.R.	Debit	Credit

Name _____

GENERAL LEDGER

Cash   ACCOUNT NO. 101

Date	Explanation	P.R.	DEBIT	CREDIT	BALANCE

Accounts Receivable   ACCOUNT NO. 106

Date	Explanation	P.R.	DEBIT	CREDIT	BALANCE

Office Supplies   ACCOUNT NO. 124

Date	Explanation	P.R.	DEBIT	CREDIT	BALANCE

Prepaid Insurance   ACCOUNT NO. 128

Date	Explanation	P.R.	DEBIT	CREDIT	BALANCE

Prepaid Rent   ACCOUNT NO. 131

Date	Explanation	P.R.	DEBIT	CREDIT	BALANCE

Office Equipment   ACCOUNT NO. 163

Date	Explanation	P.R.	DEBIT	CREDIT	BALANCE

Accounts Payable   ACCOUNT NO. 201

Date	Explanation	P.R.	DEBIT	CREDIT	BALANCE

_____, Capital   ACCOUNT NO. 301

Date	Explanation	P.R.	DEBIT	CREDIT	BALANCE

_____, Withdrawals   ACCOUNT NO. 302

Date	Explanation	P.R.	DEBIT	CREDIT	BALANCE

Name _____

Service Fees Earned**   ACCOUNT NO. 401

Date	Explanation	P.R.	DEBIT	CREDIT	BALANCE

Services Revenue*   ACCOUNT NO. 403

Date	Explanation	P.R.	DEBIT	CREDIT	BALANCE

Utilities Expense   ACCOUNT NO. 690

Date	Explanation	P.R.	DEBIT	CREDIT	BALANCE

* Problem 2-3A only.
** Problem 2-3B only

Trial Balance

Name _____

Balance Sheet

Balance Sheet

Part 2

Net Income Computation: _____

_____

_____

_____

_____

_____

_____

_____

_____

_____

_____

_____

Part 3

Debt Ratio: _____

_____

_____

_____

_____

Trial Balance

Part 2

Seven Most Likely Transactions (following order of trial balance):

(1) _____

(2) _____

(3) _____

(4) _____

(5) _____

(6) _____

(7) _____

Report of Cash Received and Cash Paid

GENERAL JOURNAL

Date	Account Titles and Explanation	P.R.	Debit	Credit

Date	Account Titles and Explanation	P.R.	Debit	Credit

Part 2

Cash   No. 101

DATE	PR	Debit	Credit	Balance

Accounts Receivable   No. 106

DATE	PR	Debit	Credit	Balance

Office Supplies   No. 108

DATE	PR	Debit	Credit	Balance

Office Equipment   No. 163

DATE	PR	Debit	Credit	Balance

Automobiles   No. 164

DATE	PR	Debit	Credit	Balance

Building   No. 170

DATE	PR	Debit	Credit	Balance

Land   No. 172

DATE	PR	Debit	Credit	Balance

Accounts Payable   No. 201

DATE	PR	Debit	Credit	Balance

Notes Payable   No. 250

DATE	PR	Debit	Credit	Balance

_____, Capital   No. 301

DATE	PR	Debit	Credit	Balance

_____, Withdrawals   No. 302

DATE	PR	Debit	Credit	Balance

Fees Earned   No. 402

DATE	PR	Debit	Credit	Balance

Salaries Expense   No. 601

DATE	PR	Debit	Credit	Balance

Utilities Expense   No. 602

DATE	PR	Debit	Credit	Balance

Trial Balance

GENERAL JOURNAL

Date	Account Titles and Explanation	P.R.	Debit	Credit

Date	Account Titles and Explanation	P.R.	Debit	Credit

Date	Account Titles and Explanation	P.R.	Debit	Credit

GENERAL LEDGER

Cash — ACCOUNT NO. 101

Date	Explanation	P.R.	DEBIT	CREDIT	BALANCE

Accounts Receivable — ACCOUNT NO. 106

Date	Explanation	P.R.	DEBIT	CREDIT	BALANCE

Computer Supplies   ACCOUNT NO. 126

Date	Explanation	P.R.	DEBIT	CREDIT	BALANCE

Prepaid Insurance   ACCOUNT NO. 128

Date	Explanation	P.R.	DEBIT	CREDIT	BALANCE

Prepaid Rent   ACCOUNT NO. 131

Date	Explanation	P.R.	DEBIT	CREDIT	BALANCE

Office Equipment   ACCOUNT NO. 163

Date	Explanation	P.R.	DEBIT	CREDIT	BALANCE

Computer Equipment   ACCOUNT NO. 167

Date	Explanation	P.R.	DEBIT	CREDIT	BALANCE

Accounts Payable   ACCOUNT NO. 201

Date	Explanation	P.R.	DEBIT	CREDIT	BALANCE

A. Lopez, Capital   ACCOUNT NO. 301

Date	Explanation	P.R.	DEBIT	CREDIT	BALANCE

A. Lopez, Withdrawals   ACCOUNT NO. 302

Date	Explanation	P.R.	DEBIT	CREDIT	BALANCE

Computer Services Revenue   ACCOUNT NO. 403

Date	Explanation	P.R.	DEBIT	CREDIT	BALANCE

Wages Expense   ACCOUNT NO. 623

Date	Explanation	P.R.	DEBIT	CREDIT	BALANCE

Advertising Expense   ACCOUNT NO. 655

Date	Explanation	P.R.	DEBIT	CREDIT	BALANCE

Mileage Expense   ACCOUNT NO. 676

Date	Explanation	P.R.	DEBIT	CREDIT	BALANCE

Miscellaneous Expense   ACCOUNT NO. 677

Date	Explanation	P.R.	DEBIT	CREDIT	BALANCE

Repairs Expense-Computer   ACCOUNT NO. 684

Date	Explanation	P.R.	DEBIT	CREDIT	BALANCE

Trial Balance

(1) _____

_____

(2) _____

_____

(3) _____

_____

_____

(4) _____

_____

_____

(5) Fast Forward: _____

_____

_____

_____

_____

Comparative Analysis--BTN 2-2

(1) Current Year Debt Ratio _____

_____

   Prior Year Debt Ratio _____

_____

(2) Current Year Debt Ratio _____

_____

   Prior Year Debt Ratio _____

_____

(3) _____

_____

_____

_____

_____

_____

_____
_____
_____
_____
_____
_____
_____
_____
_____
_____
_____
_____
_____
_____
_____
_____
_____

MEMORANDUM

TO:

FROM:

SUBJECT:

DATE:

---

(1) _____

_____

_____

_____

_____

_____

(2) _____

_____

_____

_____

_____

_____

(3) _____

_____

_____

_____

_____

_____

_____

(1) Component selected: _____

(2) (a) _____

_____

(b) _____

_____

(c) _____

_____

(d) _____

_____

(e) _____

_____

(3) Presentation Notes: _____

_____

_____

_____

_____

_____

BusinessWeek Activity--BTN 2-7

(1) _____

_____

_____

_____

(2) _____

_____

_____

(3) _____

_____

_____

_____

_____

(1) _____
                          Balance Sheet
_____

(2)

(3)

_____

_____

_____

_____

_____

_____

_____

_____

_____

_____

_____

_____

(1) _____
_____
_____
_____
_____
_____
_____

(2) _____
_____
_____
_____
_____
_____
_____
_____

(3) _____
_____
_____
_____
_____

(4) _____
_____
_____
_____
_____
_____

(1) _____
_____
_____

(2) _____
_____
_____

(3) _____
_____
_____
_____

(a) _____

(b) _____

(c) _____

(d) _____

(e) _____

Quick Study 3-2

	Dr./Cr.	Account Titles	Financial Statement
(a)	Debit		
	Credit		
(b)	Debit		
	Credit		
(c)	Debit		
	Credit		
(d)	Debit		
	Credit		
(e)	Debit		
	Credit		

Quick Study 3-3

GENERAL JOURNAL

	Date	Account Titles and Explanation	P.R	Debit	Credit
(a)					
(b)					

GENERAL JOURNAL

Date		Account Titles and Explanation	P.R	Debit	Credit
(a)					
(b)					

Quick Study 3-5

GENERAL JOURNAL

Date		Account Titles and Explanation	P.R	Debit	Credit

Quick Study 3-6

GENERAL JOURNAL

Date		Account Titles and Explanation	P.R	Debit	Credit
(a)					
(b)					

Name _____

Debit	Credit

(1) _____

(2) _____

(3) _____

Quick Study 3-8

Answer is _____

Explanation: _____

_____

_____

_____

_____

_____

Quick Study 3-9

Cash Basis: _____

_____

_____

_____

_____

Accrual Basis _____

_____

_____

_____

_____

Quick Study 3-10

Answer is _____

Explanation: _____

_____

_____

_____

_____

Chapter 3   Quick Study 3-11   *Name* _____

Profit Margin:

_____
_____
_____
_____

Interpretation of Profit Margin:

_____
_____
_____
_____
_____

Quick Study 3-12[A]

Answer is _____
Supporting work:

_____
_____
_____

Exercise 3-1

(1) _____   (4) _____
(2) _____   (5) _____
(3) _____   (6) _____

GENERAL JOURNAL

Date	Account Titles and Explanation	P.R	Debit	Credit
(a)				
(b)				
(c)				
(d)				
(e)				
(f)				

Notes: _____

_____

_____

_____

GENERAL JOURNAL

Date		Account Titles and Explanation	P.R	Debit	Credit
(a)					
(b)					
(c)					
(d)					
(e)					
(f)					
(g)					

Notes: _____

_____

_____

_____

_____

GENERAL JOURNAL

Date	Account Titles and Explanation	P.R	Debit	Credit
Adjusting Entry:				
Payday Entry:				

Exercise 3-5

(a) _____

_____

_____

(b) _____

_____

_____

(c) _____

_____

_____

(d) _____

_____

_____

(a)

GENERAL JOURNAL

Date		Account Titles and Explanation	P.R.	Debit	Credit
Adjusting Entry:					
Journal Entry (Next Period):					

(b)

GENERAL JOURNAL

Date		Account Titles and Explanation	P.R	Debit	Credit
Adjusting Entry:					
Journal Entry (Next Period):					

(c)

GENERAL JOURNAL

Date	Account Titles and Explanation	P.R.	Debit	Credit
Adjusting Entry:				
Journal Entry (Next Period):				

Exercise 3-7

Balance Sheet Insurance Asset Under:				Insurance Expense Under:	
Date of:	Accrual Basis	Cash Basis	Year	Accrual Basis	Cash Basis
12/31/2006			2006		
12/31/2007			2007		
12/31/2008			2008		
12/31/2009			2009		
			Total		

Supporting work:

Name _____

GENERAL JOURNAL

Date	Account Titles and Explanation	P.R.	Debit	Credit

Name _____

Profit Margin Calculation:

(a) _____

_____

(b) _____

_____

(c) _____

_____

(d) _____

_____

(e) _____

_____

Most Profitable: _____

_____

Interpretation of Profit Margin: _____

_____

_____

GENERAL JOURNAL

Date	Account Titles and Explanation	P.R.	Debit	Credit
(a)				
(b)				
(c)				
(d)				
(e)				
(f)				
(g)				

GENERAL JOURNAL

Date	Account Titles and Explanation	P.R.	Debit	Credit
(a)				
(b)				

(c)
Method in Part (a):

       Unearned Fees = $ _____

       Fees Earned   = $ _____

Method in Part (b):

       Unearned Fees = $ _____

       Fees Earned   = $ _____

(1) _____   (7) _____
(2) _____   (8) _____
(3) _____   (9) _____
(4) _____   (10) _____
(5) _____   (11) _____
(6) _____   (12) _____

Problem 3-2A or 3-2B
Part 1   GENERAL JOURNAL

Date	Account Titles and Explanation	P.R.	Debit	Credit

GENERAL JOURNAL

Date	Account Titles and Explanation	P.R.	Debit	Credit

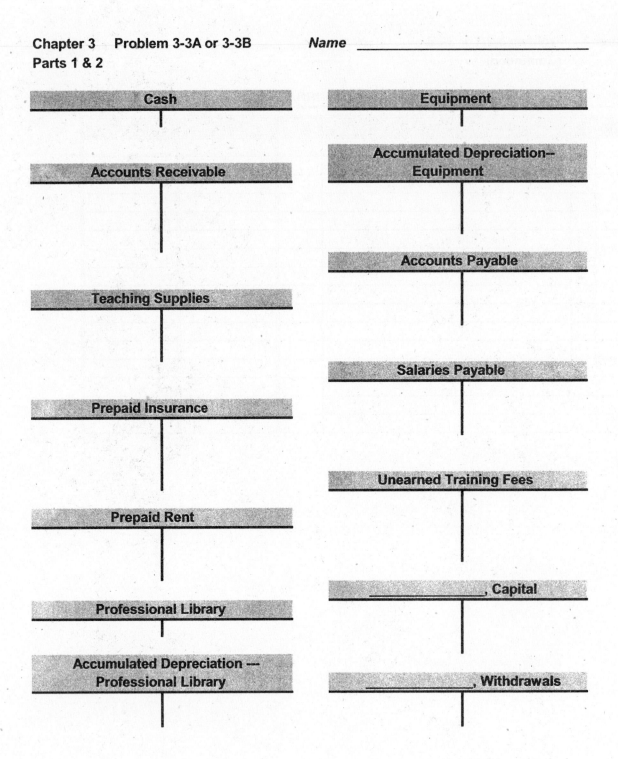

Cash	Equipment

Accounts Receivable	Accumulated Depreciation-- Equipment

Teaching Supplies	Accounts Payable

Prepaid Insurance	Salaries Payable

Prepaid Rent	Unearned Training Fees

Professional Library	_____, Capital

Accumulated Depreciation --- Professional Library	_____, Withdrawals

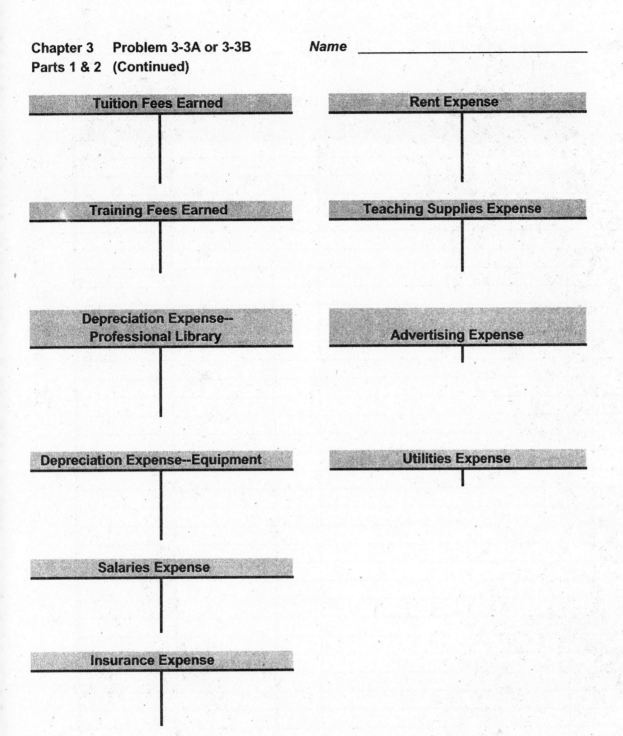

Tuition Fees Earned

Training Fees Earned

**Depreciation Expense--
Professional Library**

Depreciation Expense--Equipment

Salaries Expense

Insurance Expense

Rent Expense

Teaching Supplies Expense

Advertising Expense

Utilities Expense

GENERAL JOURNAL

Date	Account Titles and Explanation	P.R.	Debit	Credit

Adjusted Trial Balance

Income Statement

Statement of Owner's Equity

Balance Sheet

ACCOUNT TITLES	UNADJUSTED TRIAL BALANCE		ADJUSTMENTS		ADJUSTED TRIAL BALANCE	
	DR	CR	DR	CR	DR	CR

Adjustment Descriptions

(a) _____

(b) _____

(c) _____

(d) _____

(e) _____

(f) _____

(g) _____

(h) _____

Income Statement

Statement of Owner's Equity

Balance Sheet

Name _____

Income Statement

Statement of Owner's Equity

Balance Sheet

Part 2

Profit Margin:

GENERAL JOURNAL

Date	Account Titles and Explanation	P.R.	Debit	Credit

GENERAL JOURNAL

Date	Account Titles and Explanation	P.R.	Debit	Credit

_____

_____

_____

_____

_____

_____

_____

_____

_____

_____

_____

_____

_____

_____

_____

_____

_____

_____

_____

_____

_____

_____

_____

_____

Chapter 3   Serial Problem, SP 3   Name _____
Part 1   Success Systems
Journal Entries

GENERAL JOURNAL

Date	Account Titles and Explanation	P.R.	Debit	Credit

GENERAL JOURNAL

Date	Account Titles and Explanation	P.R.	Debit	Credit

GENERAL LEDGER

Cash   ACCOUNT NO. 101

Date	Explanation	P.R.	DEBIT	CREDIT	BALANCE
2007 Nov. 30	Balance				68,996

Accounts Receivable   ACCOUNT NO. 106

Date	Explanation	P.R.	DEBIT	CREDIT	BALANCE
2007 Nov. 30	Balance				15,800

Computer Supplies   ACCOUNT NO. 126

Date	Explanation	P.R.	DEBIT	CREDIT	BALANCE
2007 Nov. 30	Balance				3,350

Prepaid Insurance   ACCOUNT NO. 128

Date	Explanation	P.R.	DEBIT	CREDIT	BALANCE
2007 Nov. 30	Balance				2,400

Prepaid Rent   ACCOUNT NO. 131

Date	Explanation	P.R.	DEBIT	CREDIT	BALANCE
2007 Nov. 30	Balance				3,500

Office Equipment   ACCOUNT NO. 163

Date	Explanation	P.R.	DEBIT	CREDIT	BALANCE
2007 Nov. 30	Balance				10,000

Accumulated Depreciation--Office Equipment   ACCOUNT NO. 164

Date	Explanation	P.R.	DEBIT	CREDIT	BALANCE

Computer Equipment   ACCOUNT NO. 167

Date	Explanation	P.R.	DEBIT	CREDIT	BALANCE
2007 Nov. 30	Balance				25,000

Accumulated Depreciation--Computer Equipment   ACCOUNT NO. 168

Date	Explanation	P.R.	DEBIT	CREDIT	BALANCE

Accounts Payable   ACCOUNT NO. 201

Date	Explanation	P.R.	DEBIT	CREDIT	BALANCE
2007 Nov. 30	Balance				0

Wages Payable   ACCOUNT NO. 210

Date	Explanation	P.R.	DEBIT	CREDIT	BALANCE

Unearned Computer Services Revenue   ACCOUNT NO. 236

Date	Explanation	P.R.	DEBIT	CREDIT	BALANCE

A. Lopez, Capital   ACCOUNT NO. 301

Date	Explanation	P.R.	DEBIT	CREDIT	BALANCE
2007 Nov. 30	Balance				110,000

Name _____

A. Lopez, Withdrawals   ACCOUNT NO. 302

Date	Explanation	P.R.	DEBIT	CREDIT	BALANCE
2007 Nov. 30	Balance				6,500

Computer Services Revenue   ACCOUNT NO. 403

Date	Explanation	P.R.	DEBIT	CREDIT	BALANCE
2007 Nov. 30	Balance				32,550

Depreciation Expense--Office Equipment   ACCOUNT NO. 612

Date	Explanation	P.R.	DEBIT	CREDIT	BALANCE

Depreciation Expense--Computer Equipment   ACCOUNT NO. 613

Date	Explanation	P.R.	DEBIT	CREDIT	BALANCE

Wages Expense   ACCOUNT NO. 623

Date	Explanation	P.R.	DEBIT	CREDIT	BALANCE
2007 Nov. 30	Balance				3,150

Insurance Expense   ACCOUNT NO. 637

Date	Explanation	P.R.	DEBIT	CREDIT	BALANCE

Rent Expense   ACCOUNT NO. 640

Date	Explanation	P.R.	DEBIT	CREDIT	BALANCE

Computer Supplies Expense   ACCOUNT NO. 652

Date	Explanation	P.R.	DEBIT	CREDIT	BALANCE

Advertising Expense   ACCOUNT NO. 655

Date	Explanation	P.R.	DEBIT	CREDIT	BALANCE
2007 Nov. 30	Balance				1,790

Mileage Expense   ACCOUNT NO. 676

Date	Explanation	P.R.	DEBIT	CREDIT	BALANCE
2007 Nov. 30	Balance				864

Miscellaneous Expense   ACCOUNT NO. 677

Date	Explanation	P.R.	DEBIT	CREDIT	BALANCE
2007					
Nov. 30	Balance				300

Repairs Expense--Computer   ACCOUNT NO. 684

Date	Explanation	P.R.	DEBIT	CREDIT	BALANCE
2007					
Nov. 30	Balance				900

Income Summary   ACCOUNT NO. 901

Date	Explanation	P.R.	DEBIT	CREDIT	BALANCE

Chapter 3   Serial Problem, SP 3
Part 3   Success Systems
           (Continued)

Name _____

SUCCESS SYSTEMS
Adjusted Trial Balance
December 31, 2007

	Debit	Credit

SUCCESS SYSTEMS
Income Statement
For Three Months Ended December 31, 2007

Part 5

SUCCESS SYSTEMS
Statement of Owner's Equity
For Three Months Ended December 31, 2007

SUCCESS SYSTEMS
Balance Sheet
December 31, 2007

(1) _____

_____

_____

(2) _____

_____

_____

_____

_____

_____

_____

_____

_____

_____

_____

_____

_____

_____

(3) 2005 Profit Margin: _____

_____

_____

2004 Profit Margin: _____

_____

_____

(4) Fast Forward: _____

_____

_____

_____

_____

_____

(1) Best Buy

    Current Year Profit Margin:

    Prior Year Profit Margin:

  Circuit City

    Current Year Profit Margin:

    Prior Year Profit Margin:

(2) Analysis

(1) _____

(2) _____

(3) _____

MEMORANDUM

TO:

FROM:

SUBJECT:

DATE:

(1) _____
_____
_____
_____

(2) _____
_____
_____

(3) _____
_____
_____

(4) _____
_____
_____

(5) _____
_____
_____

(6) _____
_____
_____

Name _____

(1) _____

_____

_____

_____

_____

(2) _____

_____

_____

_____

_____

(3) _____

_____

_____

_____

_____

_____

_____

_____

_____

(4) _____

_____

_____

_____

_____

_____

(1) _____

GENERAL JOURNAL

Date		Account Titles and Explanation	P.R	Debit	Credit
(a)					
(b)					

(2) _____

_____

_____

_____

_____

_____

_____

(3) _____

_____

_____

_____

_____

_____

_____
_____
_____
_____
_____
_____
_____
_____
_____

Global Decision--BTN 3-10

(1) _____
_____
_____
_____

(2) Profit Margin _____
_____
_____
_____
_____

(3) Current Ratio for Current Year: _____
_____

Current Ratio for Prior Year: _____
_____
_____
_____

Name _____

_____

_____

_____

_____

_____

_____

_____

_____

_____

Quick Study 4-2

Steps

1st _____

2nd _____

3rd _____

4th _____

5th _____

6th _____

7th _____

8th _____

9th _____

Quick Study 4-3

(1) _____   (5) _____

(2) _____   (6) _____

(3) _____   (7) _____

(4) _____   (8) _____

Quick Study 4-4

_____

_____

_____

_____

_____

_____

_____

_____

_____

_____

_____
_____
_____
_____
_____
_____
_____
_____
_____

Quick Study 4-6

(a) _____   (d) _____
(b) _____   (e) _____
(c) _____   (f) _____

Quick Study 4-7

(a) _____   (d) _____
(b) _____   (e) _____
(c) _____

Name _____

_____ Company

Work Sheet

ACCOUNT TITLE	Unadjusted Trial Balance		Adjustments		Adjusted Trial Balance		Income Statement		Balance Sheet and Statement of Owner's Equity	
	Dr.	Cr.	Dr.	Cr.	Dr.	Cr.	Dr.	Cr.	Dr.	Cr.
Prepaid rent										
Services revenue										
Wages expense										
Accounts receivable										
Wages payable										
Rent expense										

GENERAL JOURNAL

Date		Account Titles and Explanation	P. R.	Debit	Credit

Quick Study 4-10

_____

_____

_____

Quick Study 4-11[A]

GENERAL JOURNAL

Date		Account Titles and Explanation	P. R.	Debit	Credit

Name _____

GENERAL JOURNAL

Date		Account Titles and Explanation	P. R.	Debit	Credit

Posted accounts:

M.Muncel, Capital   No. 301

DATE	PR	Debit	Credit	Balance
Mar. 31				40,000

Salaries Expense   No. 622

DATE	PR	Debit	Credit	Balance
Mar. 31				20,000

M. Muncel, Withdrawals   No. 302

DATE	PR	Debit	Credit	Balance
Mar. 31				22,000

Insurance Expense   No. 637

DATE	PR	Debit	Credit	Balance
Mar. 31				4,400

Services Revenue   No. 401

DATE	PR	Debit	Credit	Balance
Mar. 31				76,000

Rent Expense   No. 640

DATE	PR	Debit	Credit	Balance
Mar. 31				8,400

Depreciation Expense   No. 603

DATE	PR	Debit	Credit	Balance
Mar. 31				15,000

Income Summary   No. 901

DATE	PR	Debit	Credit	Balance

NO.	ACCOUNT TITLE	ADJUSTED TRIAL BALANCE		CLOSING ENTRY INFORMATION		POST-CLOSING TRIAL BALANCE	
		DR	CR	DR	CR	DR	CR

1. Closing

GENERAL JOURNAL

Date		Account Titles and Explanation	P. R.	Debit	Credit

2. Post-closing Trial Balance

Post-Closing Trial Balance

Income Statement

Statement of Owner's Equity

Balance Sheet

Name _____

Current Ratio:

_____

_____

_____

_____

_____

_____

_____

Interpretation:

_____

_____

_____

_____

_____

Exercise 4-7

	Current Assets	Current Liabilities	Current Ratio
Case 1			
Case 2			
Case 3			
Case 4			
Case 5			

Analysis:

_____

_____

_____

_____

Name _____

GENERAL JOURNAL

Date	Account Titles and Explanation	P. R.	Debit	Credit
(a)				
(b)				
(c)				
(d)				
(e)				

Exercise 4-9

(1)	(5)	(9)	(13)
(2)	(6)	(10)	(14)
(3)	(7)	(11)	(15)
(4)	(8)	(12)	(16)

NO.	ACCOUNT TITLE	ADJUSTED TRIAL BALANCE		INCOME STATEMENT		BALANCE SHEET & STATEMENT OF OWNER'S EQUITY	
		DR	CR	DR	CR	DR	Cr

Account Title	Debit	Credit
Rent earned		
Salaries expense		
Insurance expense		
Office Supplies expense		
Bike Repair expense		
Depreciation expense--Bikes		
Totals		
Net Income		
Totals		

GENERAL JOURNAL

Date	Account Titles and Explanation	P. R.	Debit	Credit

Name _____

Dylan Delivery Company
Work Sheet
For Year Ended December 31, 2008

ACCOUNT TITLE	Unadjusted Trial Balance		Adjustments		Adjusted Trial Balance		Income Statement		Balance Sheet and Statement of Owner's Equity	
	Dr.	Cr.	Dr.	Cr.	Dr.	Cr.	Dr.	Cr.	Dr.	Cr.

2. Closing Entries

GENERAL JOURNAL

Date	Account Titles and Explanation	P. R.	Debit	Credit

Capital on the Balance Sheet: _____

_____

_____

_____

_____

Chapter 4   Exercise 4-13[A]   Name _____
Part 1

GENERAL JOURNAL

Date	Account Titles and Explanation	P. R.	Debit	Credit

Part 2

GENERAL JOURNAL

Date	Account Titles and Explanation	P. R.	Debit	Credit

Part 3

GENERAL JOURNAL

Date	Account Titles and Explanation	P. R.	Debit	Credit

Chapter 4   Exercise 4-14^{A} Name _____

GENERAL JOURNAL

Date	Account Titles and Explanation	P. R.	Debit	Credit

Problem 4-1A or 4-1B

(1)	(6)	(11)	(16)
(2)	(7)	(12)	(17)
(3)	(8)	(13)	(18)
(4)	(9)	(14)	(19)
(5)	(10)	(15)	(20)

GENERAL LEDGER

Cash   ACCOUNT NO. 101

DATE	EXPLANATION	P.R.	DEBIT	CREDIT	BALANCE

Accounts Receivable   ACCOUNT NO. 106

DATE	EXPLANATION	P.R.	DEBIT	CREDIT	BALANCE

Office Supplies   ACCOUNT NO. 124

DATE	EXPLANATION	P.R.	DEBIT	CREDIT	BALANCE

Prepaid Insurance   ACCOUNT NO. 128

DATE	EXPLANATION	P.R.	DEBIT	CREDIT	BALANCE

Computer Equipment* ACCOUNT NO. 167

DATE	EXPLANATION	P.R.	DEBIT	CREDIT	BALANCE

Accumulated Depreciation-Computer Equipment* ACCOUNT NO. 168

DATE	EXPLANATION	P.R.	DEBIT	CREDIT	BALANCE

Buildings** ACCOUNT NO. 173

DATE	EXPLANATION	P.R.	DEBIT	CREDIT	BALANCE

Accumulated Depreciation-Buildings** ACCOUNT NO. 174

DATE	EXPLANATION	P.R.	DEBIT	CREDIT	BALANCE

Salaries Payable ACCOUNT NO. 209

DATE	EXPLANATION	P.R.	DEBIT	CREDIT	BALANCE

_____, Capital ACCOUNT NO. 301

DATE	EXPLANATION	P.R.	DEBIT	CREDIT	BALANCE

* Problem 4-2A only.
** Problem 4-2B only.

_____, **Withdrawals**   **ACCOUNT NO. 302**

DATE	EXPLANATION	P.R.	DEBIT	CREDIT	BALANCE

Storage Fees Earned**   **ACCOUNT NO. 401**

DATE	EXPLANATION	P.R.	DEBIT	CREDIT	BALANCE

Commissions Earned*   **ACCOUNT NO. 405**

DATE	EXPLANATION	P.R.	DEBIT	CREDIT	BALANCE

Depreciation Expense--Buildings**   **ACCOUNT NO. 606**

DATE	EXPLANATION	P.R.	DEBIT	CREDIT	BALANCE

Depreciation Expense-Computer Equipment*   **ACCOUNT NO. 612**

DATE	EXPLANATION	P.R.	DEBIT	CREDIT	BALANCE

* Problem 4-2A only.

** Problem 4-2B only.

Salaries Expense   ACCOUNT NO. 622

DATE	EXPLANATION	P.R.	DEBIT	CREDIT	BALANCE

Insurance Expense   ACCOUNT NO. 637

DATE	EXPLANATION	P.R.	DEBIT	CREDIT	BALANCE

Rent Expense   ACCOUNT NO. 640

DATE	EXPLANATION	P.R.	DEBIT	CREDIT	BALANCE

Office Supplies Expense   ACCOUNT NO. 650

DATE	EXPLANATION	P.R.	DEBIT	CREDIT	BALANCE

Repairs Expense   ACCOUNT NO. 684

DATE	EXPLANATION	P.R.	DEBIT	CREDIT	BALANCE

Telephone Expense   ACCOUNT NO. 688

DATE	EXPLANATION	P.R.	DEBIT	CREDIT	BALANCE

	Income Summary				ACCOUNT NO. 901
DATE	EXPLANATION	P.R.	DEBIT	CREDIT	BALANCE

Chapter 4   Problem 4-2A or 4-2B   Name _____
Part 2

GENERAL JOURNAL

Date	Account Titles and Explanation	P. R.	Debit	Credit

_____

Unadjusted Trial Balance

GENERAL JOURNAL

Date	Account Titles and Explanation	P. R.	Debit	Credit

Income Statement

Statement of Owner's Equity

Balance Sheet

Part 6   **(Continued)**

Closing Entries:

GENERAL JOURNAL

Date	Account Titles and Explanation	P. R.	Debit	Credit

Part 7

Post-Closing Trial Balance

_____

_____

Income Statement

_____

_____

_____

_____

_____

_____

_____

_____

_____

_____

_____

_____

_____

_____

_____

Statement of Owner's Equity

Balance Sheet

		Work Sheet					
		ADJUSTED TRIAL BALANCE		CLOSING ENTRY INFORMATION		POST-CLOSING TRIAL BALANCE	
NO.	ACCOUNT TITLES	DR	CR	DR	CR	DR	CR

GENERAL JOURNAL

Date		Account Titles and Explanation	P. R.	Debit	Credit

Financial Statement Changes:

Problem 4-4A or 4-4B
Part 1

Income Statement

Statement of Owner's Equity

Balance Sheet

GENERAL JOURNAL

Date	Account Titles and Explanation	P. R.	Debit	Credit

(a) _____

_____

_____

(b) _____

_____

_____

(c) _____

_____

_____

(d) _____

_____

_____

_____

Name _____

Work Sheet

NO.	Account Title	Unadjusted Trial Balance		Adjustments		Adjusted Trial Balance		Income Statement		Balance Sheet and Statement of Owner's Equity	
		Dr.	Cr.	Dr.	Cr.	Dr.	Cr.	Dr.	Cr.	Dr.	Cr.

GENERAL JOURNAL

Date	Account Titles and Explanation	P. R.	Debit	Credit

GENERAL JOURNAL

Date	Account Titles and Explanation	P. R.	Debit	Credit

Income Statement

Statement of Owner's Equity

_____

Balance Sheet

_____

(a)

(b)

Name _____

Work Sheet

Account Title	Unadjusted Trial Balance		Adjustments		Adjusted Trial Balance	
	Dr.	Cr.	Dr.	Cr.	Dr.	Cr.

GENERAL JOURNAL

Date	Account Titles and Explanation	P. R.	Debit	Credit

GENERAL JOURNAL

Date	Account Titles and Explanation	P. R.	Debit	Credit

Part 4

GENERAL JOURNAL

Date	Account Titles and Explanation	P. R.	Debit	Credit

Name _____

GENERAL JOURNAL

Date	Account Titles and Explanation	P. R.	Debit	Credit

GENERAL LEDGER

Cash — ACCOUNT NO. 101

Date	Explanation	P.R.	DEBIT	CREDIT	BALANCE
2007, Dec. 31	Balance				80,260

Accounts Receivable — ACCOUNT NO. 106

Date	Explanation	P.R.	DEBIT	CREDIT	BALANCE
2007, Dec. 31	Balance				5,800

Computer Supplies — ACCOUNT NO. 126

Date	Explanation	P.R.	DEBIT	CREDIT	BALANCE
2007, Dec. 31	Balance				775

Prepaid Insurance — ACCOUNT NO. 128

Date	Explanation	P.R.	DEBIT	CREDIT	BALANCE
2007, Dec. 31	Balance				1,800

Prepaid Rent — ACCOUNT NO. 131

Date	Explanation	P.R.	DEBIT	CREDIT	BALANCE
2007, Dec. 31	Balance				875

	Office Equipment			ACCOUNT NO. 163	
Date	**Explanation**	**P.R.**	**DEBIT**	**CREDIT**	**BALANCE**
2007, Dec. 31	Balance				10,000

	Accumulated Depreciation - Office Equipment			ACCOUNT NO. 164	
Date	**Explanation**	**P.R.**	**DEBIT**	**CREDIT**	**BALANCE**
2007, Dec. 31	Balance				625

	Computer Equipment			ACCOUNT NO. 167	
Date	**Explanation**	**P.R.**	**DEBIT**	**CREDIT**	**BALANCE**
2007, Dec. 31	Balance				25,000

	Accumulated Depreciation-Computer Equipment			ACCOUNT NO. 168	
Date	**Explanation**	**P.R.**	**DEBIT**	**CREDIT**	**BALANCE**
2007, Dec. 31	Balance				1,250

	Accounts Payable			ACCOUNT NO. 201	
Date	**Explanation**	**P.R.**	**DEBIT**	**CREDIT**	**BALANCE**
2007, Dec. 31	Balance				2,100

	Wages Payable			ACCOUNT NO. 210	
Date	**Explanation**	**P.R.**	**DEBIT**	**CREDIT**	**BALANCE**
2007, Dec. 31	Balance				600

Unearned Computer Services Revenue ACCOUNT NO. 236

Date	Explanation	P.R.	DEBIT	CREDIT	BALANCE
2007, Dec. 31	Balance				2,500

A. Lopez, Capital ACCOUNT NO. 301

Date	Explanation	P.R.	DEBIT	CREDIT	BALANCE
2007, Dec. 31	Balance				117,435

A. Lopez Withdrawals ACCOUNT NO. 302

Date	Explanation	P.R.	DEBIT	CREDIT	BALANCE
2007, Dec. 31	Balance				8,500

Computer Service Revenue ACCOUNT NO. 403

Date	Explanation	P.R.	DEBIT	CREDIT	BALANCE
2007, Dec. 31	Balance				36,170

Depreciation Expense-Office Equipment ACCOUNT NO. 612

Date	Explanation	P.R.	DEBIT	CREDIT	BALANCE
2007, Dec. 31	Balance				625

Depreciation Expense-Computer Equipment ACCOUNT NO. 613

Date	Explanation	P.R.	DEBIT	CREDIT	BALANCE
2007, Dec. 31	Balance				1,250

Wages Expense — ACCOUNT NO. 623

Date	Explanation	P.R.	DEBIT	CREDIT	BALANCE
2007, Dec. 31	Balance				4,650

Insurance Expense — ACCOUNT NO. 637

Date	Explanation	P.R.	DEBIT	CREDIT	BALANCE
2007, Dec. 31	Balance				600

Rent Expense — ACCOUNT NO. 640

Date	Explanation	P.R.	DEBIT	CREDIT	BALANCE
2007, Dec. 31	Balance				2,625

Computer Supplies Expense — ACCOUNT NO. 652

Date	Explanation	P.R.	DEBIT	CREDIT	BALANCE
2007, Dec. 31	Balance				4,675

Advertising Expense — ACCOUNT NO. 655

Date	Explanation	P.R.	DEBIT	CREDIT	BALANCE
2007, Dec. 31	Balance				2,990

Mileage Expense — ACCOUNT NO. 676

Date	Explanation	P.R.	DEBIT	CREDIT	BALANCE
2007, Dec. 31	Balance				1,120

Miscellaneous Expense   ACCOUNT NO. 677

Date	Explanation	P.R.	DEBIT	CREDIT	BALANCE
2007, Dec. 31	Balance				300

Repairs Expense, Computer   ACCOUNT NO. 684

Date	Explanation	P.R.	DEBIT	CREDIT	BALANCE
2007, Dec. 31	Balance				1,400

Income Summary   ACCOUNT NO. 901

Date	Explanation	P.R.	DEBIT	CREDIT	BALANCE

SUCCESS SYSTEMS
Post-Closing Trial Balance
December 31, 2007

	Debit	Credit

(1) _____

_____

_____

_____

_____

(2) _____

_____

_____

_____

_____

_____

_____

_____

_____

_____

_____

(3) _____

_____

_____

_____

(4) _____

_____

_____

(5) Fast Forward: _____

_____

_____

_____

_____

_____

_____

_____

(1) Best Buy Current Ratio: _____

   Current Year

_____

   Prior Year

_____

   Circuit City Current Ratio: _____
   Current Year

_____

   Prior Year

_____

(2) _____

_____

_____

_____

_____

(3) _____

_____

_____

_____

_____

(4) _____

_____

_____

_____

_____

(1) _____

_____

_____

_____

_____

_____

_____

_____

_____

_____

_____

_____

_____

(2) _____

_____

_____

_____

_____

_____

_____

_____

_____

_____

_____

MEMORANDUM

TO:
FROM:
SUBJECT:
DATE:

(1) _____
_____
_____
_____
_____
_____

(2) _____
_____
_____
_____
_____

(3) _____
_____
_____
_____
_____
_____

1.

Account Title	Trial Balance		Adjustments		Balance Sheet	
	Debit	Credit	Debit	Credit	Debit	Credit

2.

Account Title	Trial Balance		Adjustments		Income Statement	
	Debit	Credit	Debit	Credit	Debit	Credit

GENERAL JOURNAL

Date	Account Titles and Explanation	P. R.	Debit	Credit

3.

Account Title	Trial Balance		Adjustments		Income Statement	
	Debit	Credit	Debit	Credit	Debit	Credit

GENERAL JOURNAL

Date	Account Titles and Explanation	P.R.	Debit	Credit

4.

D. Noseworthy, Capital	Income Summary

GENERAL JOURNAL

Date	Account Titles and Explanation	P. R.	Debit	Credit

5. *Proving the Accounting Equation*

(1) _____
_____
_____
_____

(2) _____
_____
_____
_____

(3) _____
_____
_____
_____
_____
_____

Entreprenuerial Decision BTN 4-8

(1) _____
_____
_____
_____
_____
_____

(2) _____
_____
_____
_____
_____

(3) _____
_____
_____
_____
_____

(1) _____

_____

_____

(2) _____

_____

_____

(3) _____

_____

_____

(4) _____

_____

_____

(5) _____

_____

_____

Global Decision--BTN 4-10

(1) Dixon's Current Ratio: _____

   Current Year _____

_____

   Prior Year _____

_____

_____

(2) _____

_____

_____

_____

_____

GENERAL JOURNAL

Date		Account Titles and Explanation	P. R.	Debit	Credit

GENERAL JOURNAL

Date		Account Titles and Explanation	P. R.	Debit	Credit

Chapter 5   Quick Study 5-3   Name _____

Case (a)

_____
_____
_____
_____
_____
_____

Case (b)

_____
_____
_____
_____
_____
_____

Case (c)

_____
_____
_____
_____
_____
_____
_____

Case (d)

_____
_____
_____
_____
_____
_____

Interpretation of (a)

_____
_____
_____
_____

Quick Study 5-4

GENERAL JOURNAL

Date	Account Titles and Explanation	P. R.	Debit	Credit

GENERAL JOURNAL

Date	Account Titles and Explanation	P. R.	Debit	Credit

Quick Study 5-6:

Acid-Test Ratio:

_____

_____

_____

_____

Interpretation:

_____

_____

_____

_____

_____
_____
_____
_____
_____
_____
_____
_____
_____
_____
_____

Quick Study 5-8[A]

(a) _____
(b) _____
(c) _____
(d) _____
(e) _____

GENERAL JOURNAL

Date	Account Titles and Explanation	P. R.	Debit	Credit

Quick Study 5-10^A

GENERAL JOURNAL

Date	Account Titles and Explanation	P. R.	Debit	Credit

GENERAL JOURNAL

Date	Account Titles and Explanation	P. R.	Debit	Credit

(1) BUYER

GENERAL JOURNAL

Date	Account Titles and Explanation	P. R.	Debit	Credit

(2) SELLER

GENERAL JOURNAL

Date	Account Titles and Explanation	P. R.	Debit	Credit

(3)

_____
_____
_____
_____
_____
_____
_____
_____
_____
_____
_____
_____

Exercise 5-3

(1) _____	(6) _____
(2) _____	(7) _____
(3) _____	(8) _____
(4) _____	(9) _____
(5) _____	(10) _____

GENERAL JOURNAL

Date	Account Titles and Explanation	P. R.	Debit	Credit
Entries for Sale of Merchandise:				
Entries for (a):				
Entries for (b):				
Entries for (c):				

GENERAL JOURNAL

Date	Account Titles and Explanation	P. R.	Debit	Credit
Entries for Purchase of Merchandise:				
Entries for (a):				
Entries for (b):				
Entries for (c):				

GENERAL JOURNAL

Date	Account Titles and Explanation	P. R.	Debit	Credit

(1) SELLER

GENERAL JOURNAL

Date		Account Titles and Explanation	P. R.	Debit	Credit

	(a)	(b)	(c)	(d)	(e)
Sales	$ 62,000	$ 43,500	$ 46,000		$ 25,600
Cost of goods sold					
Merchandise inventory (beg.)	8,000	17,050	7,500	8,000	4,560
Total cost of merch. purchases	38,000			32,000	6,600
Merchandise inventory (ending)		(3,000)	(9,000)	(6,600)	
Cost of goods sold	34,050	16,000			7,000
Gross profit			3,750	45,600	
Expenses	10,000	10,650	12,150	3,600	6,000
Net income (loss)		$ 16,850	$ (8,400)	$ 42,000	

Work space:

Merchandise Inventory

Cost of Goods Sold

Adjusting Entries:

GENERAL JOURNAL

Date	Account Titles and Explanation	P. R.	Debit	Credit

Closing Entries:

GENERAL JOURNAL

Date	Account Titles and Explanation	P. R.	Debit	Credit

	Case X	Case Y	Case Z
Current Ratio			
Acid-Test Ratio			
Interpretation			

Chapter 5   Exercise 5-13^A   Name _____
(a) PERIODIC

GENERAL JOURNAL

Date	Account Titles and Explanation	P. R.	Debit	Credit

GENERAL JOURNAL

Date	Account Titles and Explanation	P. R.	Debit	Credit

GENERAL JOURNAL

Date	Account Titles and Explanation	P. R.	Debit	Credit

(1) BUYER

GENERAL JOURNAL

Date		Account Titles and Explanation	P. R.	Debit	Credit

(2) SELLER

GENERAL JOURNAL

Date		Account Titles and Explanation	P. R.	Debit	Credit

(1) BUYER

GENERAL JOURNAL

Date	Account Titles and Explanation	P. R.	Debit	Credit

(2) SELLER

GENERAL JOURNAL

Date	Account Titles and Explanation	P. R.	Debit	Credit

GENERAL JOURNAL

Date	Account Titles and Explanation	P. R.	Debit	Credit

GENERAL JOURNAL

Date	Account Titles and Explanation	P. R.	Debit	Credit

230

GENERAL JOURNAL

Date	Account Titles and Explanation	P. R.	Debit	Credit

GENERAL JOURNAL

Date	Account Titles and Explanation	P. R.	Debit	Credit

GENERAL JOURNAL

Date	Account Titles and Explanation	P. R.	Debit	Credit

Part 2

Income Statement

Income Statement

Part 4

Chapter 5   Problem 5-4A or 5-4B   Name _____

Part 1

_____
_____
_____
_____
_____
_____
_____
_____
_____
_____

Part 2

_____
_____
_____
_____
_____
_____
_____
_____
_____
_____

Income Statement

Part 4

Income Statement

GENERAL JOURNAL

Date	Account Titles and Explanation	P. R.	Debit	Credit

Part 3

Name _____

_____ Company

Work Sheet

For Year Ended _____

Account Title	Unadjusted Trial Balance		Adjustments		Adjusted Trial Balance		Income Statement		Balance Sheet	
	Dr.	Cr.	Dr.	Cr.	Dr.	Cr.	Dr.	Cr.	Dr.	Cr.

GENERAL JOURNAL

Date	Account Titles and Explanation	P. R.	Debit	Credit

Chapter 5   Serial Problem   Name _____
Part 1   Success Systems
Journal Entries (Continued)

Date	Account Titles and Explanation	P. R.	Debit	Credit

Date	Account Titles and Explanation	P. R.	Debit	Credit

Date	Account Titles and Explanation	P. R.	Debit	Credit

GENERAL LEDGER

Cash   ACCOUNT NO. 101

Date	Explanation	P.R.	DEBIT	CREDIT	BALANCE
2007 Dec. 31	Balance				80,260

Accounts Receivable - Alex's Engineering Co.   ACCOUNT NO. 106.1

Date	Explanation	P.R.	DEBIT	CREDIT	BALANCE
2007 Dec. 31	Balance				0

Accounts Receivable - Wildcat Services   ACCOUNT NO. 106.2

Date	Explanation	P.R.	DEBIT	CREDIT	BALANCE
2007 Dec. 31	Balance				0

Accounts Receivable - Easy Leasing   ACCOUNT NO. 106.3

Date	Explanation	P.R.	DEBIT	CREDIT	BALANCE
2007 Dec. 31	Balance				0

Accounts Receivable - Clark Co.   ACCOUNT NO. 106.4

Date	Explanation	P.R.	DEBIT	CREDIT	BALANCE
2007 Dec. 31	Balance				2,300

Accounts Receivable - Chang Corporation   ACCOUNT NO. 106.5

Date	Explanation	P.R.	DEBIT	CREDIT	BALANCE
2007 Dec. 31	Balance				0

Accounts Receivable - Gomez Co.   ACCOUNT NO. 106.6

Date	Explanation	P.R.	DEBIT	CREDIT	BALANCE
2007 Dec. 31	Balance				3,500

Accounts Receivable - Delta Co.   ACCOUNT NO. 106.7

Date	Explanation	P.R.	DEBIT	CREDIT	BALANCE
2007 Dec. 31	Balance				0

Accounts Receivable - KC, Inc.   ACCOUNT NO. 106.8

Date	Explanation	P.R.	DEBIT	CREDIT	BALANCE
2007 Dec. 31	Balance				0

Accounts Receivable - Dream, Inc.   ACCOUNT NO. 106.9

Date	Explanation	P.R.	DEBIT	CREDIT	BALANCE
2007 Dec. 31	Balance				0

Merchandise Inventory   ACCOUNT NO. 119

Date	Explanation	P.R.	DEBIT	CREDIT	BALANCE
2007 Dec. 31	Balance				0

Computer Supplies   ACCOUNT NO. 126

Date	Explanation	P.R.	DEBIT	CREDIT	BALANCE
2007 Dec. 31	Balance				775

Prepaid Insurance   ACCOUNT NO. 128

Date	Explanation	P.R.	DEBIT	CREDIT	BALANCE
2007 Dec. 31	Balance				1,800

Prepaid Rent   ACCOUNT NO. 131

Date	Explanation	P.R.	DEBIT	CREDIT	BALANCE
2007 Dec. 31	Balance				875

Office Equipment   ACCOUNT NO. 163

Date	Explanation	P.R.	DEBIT	CREDIT	BALANCE
2007 Dec. 31	Balance				10,000

Accumulated Depreciation - Office Equipment   ACCOUNT NO. 164

Date	Explanation	P.R.	DEBIT	CREDIT	BALANCE
2007 Dec. 31	Balance				625

Computer Equipment   ACCOUNT NO. 167

Date	Explanation	P.R.	DEBIT	CREDIT	BALANCE
2007 Dec. 31	Balance				25,000

Accumulated Depreciation - Computer Equipment   ACCOUNT NO. 168

Date	Explanation	P.R.	DEBIT	CREDIT	BALANCE
2007 Dec. 31	Balance				1,250

Accounts Payable — ACCOUNT NO. 201

Date	Explanation	P.R.	DEBIT	CREDIT	BALANCE
2007 Dec. 31	Balance				2,100

Wages Payable — ACCOUNT NO. 210

Date	Explanation	P.R.	DEBIT	CREDIT	BALANCE
2007 Dec. 31	Balance				600

Unearned Computer Services Revenue — ACCOUNT NO. 236

Date	Explanation	P.R.	DEBIT	CREDIT	BALANCE
2007 Dec. 31	Balance				2,500

A. Lopez, Capital — ACCOUNT NO. 301

Date	Explanation	P.R.	DEBIT	CREDIT	BALANCE
2007 Dec. 31	Balance				117,435

A. Lopez, Withdrawals — ACCOUNT NO. 302

Date	Explanation	P.R.	DEBIT	CREDIT	BALANCE
2007 Dec. 31	Balance				0

	Computer Services Revenue				ACCOUNT NO. 403
Date	Explanation	P.R.	DEBIT	CREDIT	BALANCE

	Sales				ACCOUNT NO. 413
Date	Explanation	P.R.	DEBIT	CREDIT	BALANCE

	Sales Returns and Allowances				ACCOUNT NO. 414
Date	Explanation	P.R.	DEBIT	CREDIT	BALANCE

Chapter 5 **Serial Problem**
Part 2   **Success Systems**
              (Continued)

Name _____

Sales Discounts   ACCOUNT NO. 415

Date	Explanation	P.R.	DEBIT	CREDIT	BALANCE

Cost of Goods Sold   ACCOUNT NO. 502

Date	Explanation	P.R.	DEBIT	CREDIT	BALANCE

Depreciation Expense-Office Equipment   ACCOUNT NO. 612

Date	Explanation	P.R.	DEBIT	CREDIT	BALANCE

Depreciation Expense-Computer Equipment   ACCOUNT NO. 613

Date	Explanation	P.R.	DEBIT	CREDIT	BALANCE

Wages Expense   ACCOUNT NO. 623

Date	Explanation	P.R.	DEBIT	CREDIT	BALANCE

Insurance Expense   ACCOUNT NO. 637

Date	Explanation	P.R.	DEBIT	CREDIT	BALANCE

Rent Expense   ACCOUNT NO. 640

Date	Explanation	P.R.	DEBIT	CREDIT	BALANCE

Computer Supplies Expense   ACCOUNT NO. 652

Date	Explanation	P.R.	DEBIT	CREDIT	BALANCE

Advertising Expense   ACCOUNT NO. 655

Date	Explanation	P.R.	DEBIT	CREDIT	BALANCE

Mileage Expense   ACCOUNT NO. 676

Date	Explanation	P.R.	DEBIT	CREDIT	BALANCE

Miscellaneous Expense   ACCOUNT NO. 677

Date	Explanation	P.R.	DEBIT	CREDIT	BALANCE

Repairs Expense - Computer   ACCOUNT NO. 684

Date	Explanation	P.R.	DEBIT	CREDIT	BALANCE

Name _____

SUCCESS SYSTEMS
Partial Work Sheet
March 31, 2008

Acct. No.	ACCOUNT TITLES	UNADJUSTED TRIAL BALANCE		ADJUSTMENTS		ADJUSTED TRIAL BALANCE	
		Dr.	Cr.	Dr.	Cr.	Dr.	Cr.

SUCCESS SYSTEMS

Income Statement

For Three Months Ended March 31, 2008

Part 5

SUCCESS SYSTEMS

Statement of Owner's Equity

For Three Months Ended March 31, 2008

SUCCESS SYSTEMS
Balance Sheet
March 31, 2008

Part 1

_____
_____
_____
_____
_____
_____
_____
_____

Part 2

_____
_____
_____
_____
_____
_____
_____
_____
_____
_____
_____
_____
_____
_____
_____
_____
_____

Part 3
Fast Forward:

_____
_____
_____
_____
_____
_____
_____
_____
_____

Part 1

_____
_____
_____
_____
_____
_____
_____
_____
_____
_____
_____
_____
_____
_____
_____
_____
_____

Part 2

_____
_____
_____
_____
_____
_____
_____

Part 3

_____
_____
_____
_____
_____
_____

Part 1

_____
_____
_____
_____
_____
_____
_____
_____
_____
_____
_____
_____
_____

Part 2

_____
_____
_____
_____
_____
_____
_____
_____

MEMORANDUM

TO:

FROM:

SUBJECT:

DATE:

	2004	2003	2002
Fiscal Year ($ thousands)			
Net sales			
Cost of goods sold			
Gross margin			
Gross margin ratio			

Analysis:

(1a)

_____
_____
_____
_____
_____
_____
_____
_____

(1b)

_____
_____
_____
_____
_____
_____
_____
_____

(1c)

_____
_____
_____
_____
_____
_____
_____

(1d)

_____
_____
_____
_____
_____

_____

_____

_____

_____

_____

_____

_____

_____

(2)

Check: Net Income is _____.

_____

(3)

_____

_____

_____

_____

_____

_____

_____

(1) _____
_____
_____
_____
_____

(2)   GENERAL JOURNAL

Date	Account Titles and Explanation	P. R.	Debit	Credit

(3)   GENERAL JOURNAL

Date	Account Titles and Explanation	P. R.	Debit	Credit

(4) _____
_____
_____
_____
_____
_____

(5) _____
_____
_____
_____

(6) _____
_____
_____
_____
_____

CoCaLo
Forecasted Income Statement
For Year Ended January 31, 2008

_____
_____
_____
_____
_____
_____
_____
_____

Part 2

_____
_____
_____
_____
_____
_____
_____
_____
_____
_____

Part 3

_____
_____
_____
_____
_____
_____
_____
_____
_____
_____
_____
_____
_____

_____
_____
_____
_____
_____
_____
_____
_____
_____
_____
_____
_____
_____
_____
_____
_____
_____
_____
_____
_____
_____
_____
_____
_____
_____
_____

(1) _____

_____

_____

_____

_____

_____

_____

_____

(2) _____

_____

_____

_____

_____

_____

_____

(3) _____

_____

_____

_____

_____

_____

a) FIFO

Date	Purchases	Cost of Goods Sold	Inventory Balance

b) LIFO

Date	Purchases	Cost of Goods Sold	Inventory Balance

c) Weighted Average

Date	Purchases	Cost of Goods Sold	Inventory Balance

Quick Study 6-2

a) FIFO

Date	Purchases	Cost of Goods Sold	Inventory Balance

b) LIFO

Date	Purchases	Cost of Goods Sold	Inventory Balance

c) Weighted Average

Date	Purchases	Cost of Goods Sold	Inventory Balance

d) Specific Identification

(1) _____

(2) _____

(3) _____

(4) _____

(5) _____

Quick Study 6-5

(1) _____

_____

_____

(2) _____

_____

_____

_____
_____
_____
_____
_____
_____

Quick Study 6-7

_____
_____
_____
_____
_____
_____

Quick Study 6-8

_____
_____
_____
_____
_____

Quick Study 6-9

Inventory Items	Units	Per Unit		Total Cost	Total Market	LCM applied to	
		Cost	Market			Items	Whole

(a) LCM applied to whole: _____

(b) LCM applied to products: _____

(a) _____

_____

(b) _____

_____

(c) _____

_____

(d) _____

_____

(e) _____

_____

(f) _____

_____

Quick Study 6-11

Inventory Turnover _____

_____

_____

Day's Sales in Inventory _____

_____

_____

_____

Quick Study 6-12^{A}

(a) _____

_____

(b) _____

_____

(c) _____

_____

_____

(a) _____

_____

_____

(b) _____

_____

_____

(c) _____

_____

_____

(d) _____

_____

Quick Study 6-14[B]

_____

_____

_____

_____

_____

_____

_____

Exercise 6-1
(a) Specific Identification

_____

_____

_____

_____

_____

_____

(b) Weighted Average Perpetual

Date	Purchases	Cost of Goods Sold	Inventory Balance

(c) FIFO Perpetual

Date	Purchases	Cost of Goods Sold	Inventory Balance

(d) LIFO Perpetual

Date	Purchases	Cost of Goods Sold	Inventory Balance

	Specific Identification	Weighted Average	FIFO	LIFO
LAKER COMPANY				
Income Statements				
For Month Ended January 31				

(1) _____

_____

(2) _____

_____

(3) _____

_____

_____

(a) FIFO Perpetual

Date	Purchases	Cost of Goods Sold	Inventory Balance

FIFO Gross Margin:

(a) LIFO Perpetual

Date	Purchases	Cost of Goods Sold	Inventory Balance

LIFO Gross Margin:

Specific Identification Method

(a) Ending Inventory and Cost of Goods Sold: _____

_____

_____

_____

_____

_____

_____

_____

_____

_____

_____

_____

_____

(b) Gross Margin: _____

_____

_____

_____

_____

_____

Inventory Items	Units	Per Unit		Total Cost	Total Market	LCM applied to:	
		Cost	Market			Products	Whole

(a) LCM applied to whole: _____

(b) LCM applied to products: _____

Exercise 6-6

(1) Gross Profit _____

_____

_____

(2)

	2007	2008	2009
Sales			
Cost of goods sold			
Beginning inventory			
Cost of Purchases			
Goods avail. for sale			
Ending Inventory			
Cost of goods sold			
Gross Profit			

Inventory Turnover (2007):

_____
_____
_____
_____

Inventory Turnover (2008):

_____
_____
_____
_____

Days' Sales in Inventory (2007):

_____
_____
_____
_____

Days' Sales in Inventory (2008):

_____
_____
_____
_____

Analysis Comments:

_____
_____
_____
_____

Name _____

(1) (a) _____

_____

_____

_____

_____

_____

_____

(b) _____

_____

_____

_____

_____

_____

_____

(2) _____

_____

_____

_____

_____

_____

_____

Method and Computations	Ending Inventory	Cost of Goods Sold
(a) Specific Identification		

(b) Weighted Average Periodic

(c) FIFO Periodic

(d) LIFO Periodic

Chapter 6   Exercise 6-10^{A} Name _____

Method and Computations	Ending Inventory	Cost of Goods Sold
(a) FIFO Periodic		

(b) LIFO Periodic

(c) FIFO Gross Margin:

LIFO Gross Margin

Method and Computations	Ending Inventory	Cost of Goods Sold
(a) Specific Identification		
(b) Weighted Average Periodic		
(c) FIFO Periodic		
(d) LIFO Periodic		

Income Effect(s): _____

_____

_____

	Ending Inventory	Cost of Goods Sold
Method and Computations		
(a) Specific Identification		
(b) Weighted Average Periodic		
(c) FIFO Periodic		
(d) LIFO Periodic		

Income Effect(s): _____

	At Cost	At Retail

Exercise 6-14[B]

(1) Cost of Goods Available for Sale and Units Available for Sale:

_____

_____

_____

_____

_____

_____

_____

_____

_____

_____

(2) Ending Inventory (in Units):

_____

_____

_____

_____

(3a) FIFO Perpetual

Date	Purchases	Cost of Goods Sold	Inventory Balance

(3b) LIFO Perpetual

Date	Purchases	Cost of Goods Sold	Inventory Balance

(3c) Specific Identification

(3d) Weighted Average Perpetual

Date	Purchases	Cost of Goods Sold	Inventory Balance

(4) Gross Profit

	FIFO	LIFO	Specific Identification	Weighted Average
Sales				
Cost of goods sold				
Gross profit				

(5) _____

Part 1

(a) Cost of Goods Sold	2007	2008	2009
Reported............................			
Adjustments: 12/31/2007 error			
12/31/2008 error			
Corrected................................			

(b) Net Income	2007	2008	2009
Reported............................			
Adjustments: 12/31/2007 error			
12/31/2008 error			
Corrected................................			

(c) Total Current Assets	2007	2008	2009
Reported............................			
Adjustments: 12/31/2007 error			
12/31/2008 error			
Corrected................................			

(d) Equity	2007	2008	2009
Reported............................			
Adjustments: 12/31/2007 error			
12/31/2008 error			
Corrected................................			

Part 2

_____
_____
_____
_____
_____
_____

Part 3

_____
_____
_____
_____
_____
_____
_____
_____

Inventory Items	Units	Per Unit		Total Cost	Total Market	LCM applied to		
		Cost	Market			Items	Categories	Whole

(a) _____

_____

(b) _____

_____

(c) _____

_____

_____

Part 1

Units Available for Sale and Cost of Units Available for Sale:

_____
_____
_____
_____
_____
_____
_____
_____

Part 2

(a) FIFO Periodic

_____
_____
_____
_____
_____
_____
_____
_____
_____

(b) LIFO Periodic

_____
_____
_____
_____
_____
_____
_____
_____

(c) Weighted Average Periodic

_____
_____
_____
_____
_____
_____
_____

Comparative Income Statements

Income Statements Comparing FIFO, LIFO and Weighted Average
For Year Ended December 31, 2008

	FIFO	LIFO	Weighted Average

Supporting Calculations:

_____
_____
_____
_____
_____
_____
_____

Part 3
Advantages:
_____LIFO_____
_____
_____FIFO_____
_____

Disadvantages:
_____LIFO_____
_____
_____FIFO_____
_____

_____ Company Estimated Inventory December 31	At Cost	At Retail

Part 2

_____ Company Inventory Shortage December 31	At Cost	At Retail

_____ Company
Estimated Inventory
March 31

Success Systems

Part A

1.

Inventory Items	Units	Per Unit Cost	Per Unit Market	Total Cost	Total Market	LCM applied to: Items	LCM applied to: Whole

2.

Inventory Items	Units	Per Unit Cost	Per Unit Market	Total Cost	Total Market	LCM applied to: Items	LCM applied to: Whole

Part B

(1) Inventory Turnover:

(1) Days' Sales in Inventory:

(2) Analysis:

(1) _____

_____

(2) 2005: _____

_____

_____

2004: _____

_____

_____

_____

(3) _____

_____

_____

_____

_____

(4) _____
_____
_____
_____
_____

(5)
(a) Inventory Turnover: _____
_____
_____
_____

(b) Days' Sales in Inventory: _____
_____
_____
_____

(6) Fast Forward: _____
_____
_____
_____
_____
_____
_____
_____
_____
_____
_____
_____
_____
_____

(1)

Inventory Turnover--Best Buy:

_____
_____
_____
_____
_____

Inventory Turnover--Circuit City:

_____
_____
_____
_____
_____
_____

(2)

Days' Sales in Inventory -- Best Buy:

_____
_____
_____
_____
_____
_____
_____

Days' Sales in Inventory -- Circuit City:

_____
_____
_____
_____
_____
_____
_____

(3) Interpretation:

_____
_____
_____
_____
_____
_____
_____
_____

(1) Profit Margin: _____

_____

_____

_____

_____

_____

Current Ratio: _____

_____

_____

_____

_____

_____

(2) _____

_____

_____

_____

_____

_____

_____

_____

_____

_____

_____

_____

_____

MEMORANDUM

TO:

FROM:

SUBJECT:

DATE:

(1) _____
_____
_____

(2) _____
_____

(3) Gross Margin: _____
_____
_____

Gross Margin Ratio: _____
_____

(4) _____

Inventory Turnover: _____
_____
_____

Days' Sales in Inventory _____
_____
_____
_____
_____

Teamwork in Action--BTN 6-6

(a) and (b) Concept discussion: _____
_____
_____
_____
_____
_____
_____
_____
_____
_____
_____
_____
_____

(a) and (b) Procedures:

Date	Purchases	Cost of Goods Sold	Inventory Balance

(c)

(d)

(e)

_____
_____
_____
_____
_____
_____
_____
_____
_____
_____
_____
_____
_____
_____

Entrepreneurial Decision--BTN 6-8

(1)(a) Inventory Turnover _____
_____
_____

Day's Sales in Inventory _____
_____
_____

(b) Inventory Turnover _____
_____
_____

Day's Sales in Inventory _____
_____
_____

(2) _____
_____
_____
_____
_____
_____
_____
_____

_____
_____
_____
_____
_____
_____
_____
_____
_____
_____
_____
_____
_____
_____
_____

Global Decision--BTN 6-10

(1) Inventory Turnover--Dixons:
_____
_____
_____
_____
_____
_____
_____

Days' Sales in Inventory--Dixons:
_____
_____
_____
_____
_____
_____
_____

(2) Interpretation:
_____
_____
_____
_____
_____

(1) _____

(2) _____

(3) _____

(4) _____

(5) _____

Quick Study 7-2

(1) _____

(2) _____

(3) _____

(4) _____

Quick Study 7-3

(1) _____   (7) _____

(2) _____   (8) _____

(3) _____   (9) _____

(4) _____   (10) _____

(5) _____   (11) _____

(6) _____   (12) _____

Quick Study 7-4

(a) _____

(b) _____

(c) _____

(d) _____

(e) _____

(f) _____

(g) _____

(h) _____

GENERAL JOURNAL

Date	Account Titles and Explanation	P. R.	Debit	Credit

Quick Study 7-6

Segment	Segment Income	Average Segment Assets	Segment return on Assets

Interpretation:

_____

_____

_____

_____

Product	Product Sales	Percent of Total Sales

Interpretation:

_____

_____

_____

	SALES JOURNAL				
Date	Account Debited	Invoice Number	PR	Accts. Rec. Dr. Sales Cr.	Cost of Goods Sold Dr. Inventory Cr.

Exercise 7-2

March 2 _____

5 _____

7 _____

8 _____

12 _____

16 _____

19 _____

25 _____

SALES JOURNAL				
Date	Account Debited	Invoice Number	PR	Accts. Rec. Dr. Sales Cr.

Exercise 7-4

CASH RECEIPTS JOURNAL								
Date	Account Credited	Explanation	PR	Cash Dr.	Sales Discount Dr.	Accts. Rec. Cr.	Sales Cr.	Other Accts. Cr.	Cost of Goods Sold Dr. Inv. Cr.

Exercise 7-5

Nov.	3	
	7	
	9	
	13	
	18	
	22	
	27	
	30	

Exercise 7-6[A]

CASH RECEIPTS JOURNAL							
Date	Account Credited	Explanation	PR	Cash Dr.	Sales Discount Dr.	Accts. Rec. Cr.	Sales Cr.	Other Accts. Cr.

PURCHASES JOURNAL

Date	Account	Date of Invoice	Terms	PR	Accts. Payable Cr.	Inventory Dr.	Office Supplies Dr.	Other Accts. Dr.

Exercise 7-8

June	1	
	8	
	14	
	17	
	24	
	28	
	29	

Exercise 7-9^A

PURCHASES JOURNAL

Date	Account	Date of Invoice	Terms	PR	Accts. Payable Cr.	Purchases Dr.	Office Supplies Dr.	Other Accts. Dr.

Exercise 7-10

CASH DISBURSEMENTS JOURNAL

Date	Ck. No.	Payee	Account Debited	PR	Cash Cr.	Inventory Cr.	Other Accts. Dr.	Accts. Payable Dr.

April 3 _____
       9 _____
      12 _____
      17 _____
      20 _____
      28 _____
      29 _____
      30 _____

Exercise 7-12[A]

						CASH DISBURSEMENTS JOURNAL			
Date	Ck. No.	Payee	Account Debited	PR	Cash Cr.	Purchases Discounts Cr.	Other Accts. Dr.	Accts. Payable Dr.

Exercise 7-13

(a) _____
_____
_____
_____

(b) _____
_____
_____

ACCOUNTS RECEIVABLE SUBSIDIARY LEDGER

Anna Page	Sara Reed	Aaron Reckers

Part 2

GENERAL LEDGER

Accounts Receivable	Sales	Sales Returns and Allowances

Inventory	Cost of Goods Sold

Schedule of Accounts Receivable

Accounts Receivable Controlling Account

ACCOUNTS RECEIVABLE LEDGER

Eric Horner

Hong Jiang

Joe Mack

Tess Cox

Part 2

GENERAL LEDGER

Accounts Receivable

Sales

Part 3

_____

Schedule of Accounts Receivable

(1) _____

(2) _____

(3) _____

(4) _____

(5) _____

Exercise 7-17

Segment	Segment Income (in $ mil.)		Segment Assets (in $ mil.)		Segment Return on Assets
	2007	2006	2007	2006	2007

Analysis and Interpretation: _____

_____

_____

_____

_____

_____

_____

_____

				Sales Journal	Page 3
Date	Account Debited	Invoice Number	PR	Accts. Receivable Dr. Sales Cr.	Cost of Goods Sold Dr. Inventory Cr.

				Cash Receipts Journal					Page 3
Date	Account Credited	Explanation	PR	Cash Dr.	Sales Disc. Dr.	Accts. Rec. Cr.	Sales Cr.	Other Accts. Cr.	Cost of Goods Sold Dr. Inv. Cr.

GENERAL LEDGER

Cash   ACCOUNT NO. 101

Date	Explanation	P.R.	DEBIT	CREDIT	BALANCE

Accounts Receivable   ACCOUNT NO. 106

Date	Explanation	P.R.	DEBIT	CREDIT	BALANCE

Inventory   ACCOUNT NO. 119

Date	Explanation	P.R.	DEBIT	CREDIT	BALANCE

Long-Term Notes Payable   ACCOUNT NO. 251

Date	Explanation	P.R.	DEBIT	CREDIT	BALANCE

Sales   ACCOUNT NO. 413

Date	Explanation	P.R.	DEBIT	CREDIT	BALANCE

Sales Discounts   ACCOUNT NO. 415

Date	Explanation	P.R.	DEBIT	CREDIT	BALANCE

Cost of Goods Sold   ACCOUNT NO. 502

Date	Explanation	P.R.	DEBIT	CREDIT	BALANCE

ACCOUNTS RECEIVABLE LEDGER

Date	Explanation	P.R.	DEBIT	CREDIT	BALANCE

Date	Explanation	P.R.	DEBIT	CREDIT	BALANCE

Date	Explanation	P.R.	DEBIT	CREDIT	BALANCE

Trial Balance

Schedule of Accounts Receivable

Part 5

Analysis: _____

	Sales Journal			Page 3
Date	Account Debited	Invoice Number	PR	Accts Receivable Dr. Sales Cr.

		Cash Receipts Journal						Page 3
Date	Account Credited	Explanation	PR	Cash Dr.	Sales Discount Dr.	Accts. Rec. Cr.	Sales Cr.	Other Accts. Cr.

GENERAL LEDGER

Cash   ACCOUNT NO. 101

Date	Explanation	P.R.	DEBIT	CREDIT	BALANCE

Accounts Receivable   ACCOUNT NO. 106

Date	Explanation	P.R.	DEBIT	CREDIT	BALANCE

Inventory   ACCOUNT NO. 119

Date	Explanation	P.R.	DEBIT	CREDIT	BALANCE

Long-Term Notes Payable   ACCOUNT NO. 251

Date	Explanation	P.R.	DEBIT	CREDIT	BALANCE

Sales   ACCOUNT NO. 413

Date	Explanation	P.R.	DEBIT	CREDIT	BALANCE

Sales Discounts   ACCOUNT NO. 415

Date	Explanation	P.R.	DEBIT	CREDIT	BALANCE

ACCOUNTS RECEIVABLE LEDGER

Date	Explanation	P.R.	DEBIT	CREDIT	BALANCE

Date	Explanation	P.R.	DEBIT	CREDIT	BALANCE

Date	Explanation	P.R.	DEBIT	CREDIT	BALANCE

Trial Balance

Schedule of Accounts Receivable

Part 5

Analysis Component:

					Accts. Payable Cr.	Inventory Dr.	Office Supplies Dr.	Other Accts. Dr.
Purchases Journal								**Page 3**
Date	Account	Date of Invoice	Terms	PR	Accts. Payable Cr.	Inventory Dr.	Office Supplies Dr.	Other Accts. Dr.

Cash Disbursements Journal								**Page 3**
Date	Ck. No.	Payee	Account Debited	PR	Cash Cr.	Inventory Cr.	Other Accts. Dr.	Accts. Payable Dr.

GENERAL JOURNAL   Page 3

Date	Account Titles and Explanation	P. R.	Debit	Credit

GENERAL LEDGER

Cash   ACCOUNT NO. 101

Date	Explanation	P.R.	DEBIT	CREDIT	BALANCE

Inventory   ACCOUNT NO. 119

Date	Explanation	P.R.	DEBIT	CREDIT	BALANCE

Office Supplies   ACCOUNT NO. 124

Date	Explanation	P.R.	DEBIT	CREDIT	BALANCE

Store Supplies   ACCOUNT NO. 125

Date	Explanation	P.R.	DEBIT	CREDIT	BALANCE

Store Equipment   ACCOUNT NO. 165

Date	Explanation	P.R.	DEBIT	CREDIT	BALANCE

Accounts Payable   ACCOUNT NO. 201

Date	Explanation	P.R.	DEBIT	CREDIT	BALANCE

Long-Term Notes Payable   ACCOUNT NO. 251

Date	Explanation	P.R.	DEBIT	CREDIT	BALANCE

Sales Salaries Expense   ACCOUNT NO. 621

Date	Explanation	P.R.	DEBIT	CREDIT	BALANCE

Advertising Expense   ACCOUNT NO. 655

Date	Explanation	P.R.	DEBIT	CREDIT	BALANCE

ACCOUNTS PAYABLE LEDGER

Date	Explanation	P.R.	DEBIT	CREDIT	BALANCE

Date	Explanation	P.R.	DEBIT	CREDIT	BALANCE

Date	Explanation	P.R.	DEBIT	CREDIT	BALANCE

Date	Explanation	P.R.	DEBIT	CREDIT	BALANCE

Part 4

Trial Balance

Schedule of Accounts Payable

Purchases Journal								Page 3
Date	Account	Date of Invoice	Terms	PR	Accts. Payable Cr.	Purchases Dr.	Office Supplies Dr.	Other Accts. Dr.

Cash Disbursements Journal								Page 3
Date	Ck. No.	Payee	Account Debited	PR	Cash Cr.	Purchases Discount Cr.	Other Accts. Dr.	Accts. Payable Dr.

GENERAL JOURNAL   Page 3

Date	Account Titles and Explanation	P. R.	Debit	Credit

GENERAL LEDGER

Cash   ACCOUNT NO. 101

Date	Explanation	P.R.	DEBIT	CREDIT	BALANCE

Inventory   ACCOUNT NO. 119

Date	Explanation	P.R.	DEBIT	CREDIT	BALANCE

Office Supplies   ACCOUNT NO. 124

Date	Explanation	P.R.	DEBIT	CREDIT	BALANCE

Store Supplies   ACCOUNT NO. 125

Date	Explanation	P.R.	DEBIT	CREDIT	BALANCE

Store Equipment   ACCOUNT NO. 165

Date	Explanation	P.R.	DEBIT	CREDIT	BALANCE

Accounts Payable   ACCOUNT NO. 201

Date	Explanation	P.R.	DEBIT	CREDIT	BALANCE

Long-Term Notes Payable   ACCOUNT NO. 251

Date	Explanation	P.R.	DEBIT	CREDIT	BALANCE

Purchases   ACCOUNT NO. 505

Date	Explanation	P.R.	DEBIT	CREDIT	BALANCE

Purchase Returns and Allowances   ACCOUNT NO. 506

Date	Explanation	P.R.	DEBIT	CREDIT	BALANCE

Purchase Discounts   ACCOUNT NO. 507

Date	Explanation	P.R.	DEBIT	CREDIT	BALANCE

Sales Salaries Expense   ACCOUNT NO. 621

Date	Explanation	P.R.	DEBIT	CREDIT	BALANCE

Advertising Expense   ACCOUNT NO. 655

Date	Explanation	P.R.	DEBIT	CREDIT	BALANCE

ACCOUNTS PAYABLE LEDGER

Date	Explanation	P.R.	DEBIT	CREDIT	BALANCE

Date	Explanation	P.R.	DEBIT	CREDIT	BALANCE

Date	Explanation	P.R.	DEBIT	CREDIT	BALANCE

Date	Explanation	P.R.	DEBIT	CREDIT	BALANCE

Trial Balance

Schedule of Accounts Payable

Sales Journal					Page 2
Date	Account Debited	Invoice Number	PR	Accts. Rec. Dr. Sales Cr.	Cost of Goods Sold Dr. Inventory Cr.

Cash Receipts Journal									Page 2
Date	Account Credited	Explanation	PR	Cash Dr.	Sales Disc. Dr.	Accts. Rec. Cr.	Sales Cr.	Other Accts. Cr.	Cost of Goods Sold Dr. Inv. Cr.

		Date of Inv.			Accts. Pay. Cr.	Inventory Dr.	Office Supplies Dr.	Other Accts. Dr.
Date	Account		Terms	PR				

Purchase Journal — Page 2

Date	Ck. No.	Payee	Account Debited	PR	Cash Cr.	Inventory Cr.	Other Accts. Dr.	Accts. Payable Dr.

Cash Disbursements Journal — Page 2

GENERAL JOURNAL   Page 2

Date	Account Titles and Explanation	PR	Debit	Credit

GENERAL LEDGER

Cash   ACCOUNT NO. 101

Date	Explanation	P.R.	DEBIT	CREDIT	BALANCE

Accounts Receivable   ACCOUNT NO. 106

Date	Explanation	P.R.	DEBIT	CREDIT	BALANCE

Inventory   ACCOUNT NO. 119

Date	Explanation	P.R.	DEBIT	CREDIT	BALANCE

Office Supplies   ACCOUNT NO. 124

Date	Explanation	P.R.	DEBIT	CREDIT	BALANCE

Store Supplies   ACCOUNT NO. 125

Date	Explanation	P.R.	DEBIT	CREDIT	BALANCE

Office Equipment   ACCOUNT NO. 163

Date	Explanation	P.R.	DEBIT	CREDIT	BALANCE

Accounts Payable — ACCOUNT NO. 201

Date	Explanation	P.R.	DEBIT	CREDIT	BALANCE

Long-Term Notes Payable — ACCOUNT NO. 251

Date	Explanation	P.R.	DEBIT	CREDIT	BALANCE

_____, Capital — ACCOUNT NO. 301

Date	Explanation	P.R.	DEBIT	CREDIT	BALANCE

Sales — ACCOUNT NO. 413

Date	Explanation	P.R.	DEBIT	CREDIT	BALANCE

Sales Discounts — ACCOUNT NO. 415

Date	Explanation	P.R.	DEBIT	CREDIT	BALANCE

Cost of Goods Sold — ACCOUNT NO. 502

Date	Explanation	P.R.	DEBIT	CREDIT	BALANCE

Sales Salaries Expense   ACCOUNT NO. 621

Date	Explanation	P.R.	DEBIT	CREDIT	BALANCE

ACCOUNTS RECEIVABLE LEDGER

Date	Explanation	P.R.	DEBIT	CREDIT	BALANCE

Date	Explanation	P.R.	DEBIT	CREDIT	BALANCE

Date	Explanation	P.R.	DEBIT	CREDIT	BALANCE

ACCOUNTS PAYABLE LEDGER

Date	Explanation	P.R.	DEBIT	CREDIT	BALANCE

Date	Explanation	P.R.	DEBIT	CREDIT	BALANCE

Date	Explanation	P.R.	DEBIT	CREDIT	BALANCE

Date	Explanation	P.R.	DEBIT	CREDIT	BALANCE

Trial Balance

Schedule of Accounts Receivable

Schedule of Accounts Payable

		Sales Journal			Page 2
Date	Account Debited	Invoice Number	PR	Accts. Receivable Dr. Sales Cr.	

			Cash Receipts Journal					Page 2
Date	Account Credited	Explanation	PR	Cash Dr.	Sales Disc. Dr.	Accts. Rec. Cr.	Sales Cr.	Other Accts. Cr.

					Purchases Journal			Page 2
Date	Account	Date of Invoice	Terms	PR	Accts. Payable Cr.	Purchases Dr.	Office Supplies Dr.	Other Accts. Dr.

					Cash Disbursements Journal			Page 2
Date	Ck. No.	Payee	Account Debited	PR	Cash Cr.	Purch. Disc. Cr.	Other Accts. Dr.	Accts. Payable Dr.

GENERAL JOURNAL   Page 2

Date	Account Titles and Explanation	P. R.	Debit	Credit

GENERAL LEDGER

Cash   ACCOUNT NO. 101

Date	Explanation	P.R.	DEBIT	CREDIT	BALANCE

Accounts Receivable   ACCOUNT NO. 106

Date	Explanation	P.R.	DEBIT	CREDIT	BALANCE

Inventory   ACCOUNT NO. 119

Date	Explanation	P.R.	DEBIT	CREDIT	BALANCE

Office Supplies   ACCOUNT NO. 124

Date	Explanation	P.R.	DEBIT	CREDIT	BALANCE

Store Supplies   ACCOUNT NO. 125

Date	Explanation	P.R.	DEBIT	CREDIT	BALANCE

Office Equipment   ACCOUNT NO. 163

Date	Explanation	P.R.	DEBIT	CREDIT	BALANCE

			Accounts Payable				ACCOUNT NO. 201
Date	Explanation	P.R.	DEBIT	CREDIT	BALANCE

			Long-Term Notes Payable			ACCOUNT NO. 251
Date	Explanation	P.R.	DEBIT	CREDIT	BALANCE

			_____, Capital		ACCOUNT NO. 301
Date	Explanation	P.R.	DEBIT	CREDIT	BALANCE

			Sales			ACCOUNT NO. 413
Date	Explanation	P.R.	DEBIT	CREDIT	BALANCE

			Sales Discounts		ACCOUNT NO. 415
Date	Explanation	P.R.	DEBIT	CREDIT	BALANCE

			Purchases		ACCOUNT NO. 505
Date	Explanation	P.R.	DEBIT	CREDIT	BALANCE

Purchases Returns and Allowances   ACCOUNT NO. 506

Date	Explanation	P.R.	DEBIT	CREDIT	BALANCE

Purchases Discount   ACCOUNT NO. 507

Date	Explanation	P.R.	DEBIT	CREDIT	BALANCE

Sales Salaries Expense   ACCOUNT NO. 621

Date	Explanation	P.R.	DEBIT	CREDIT	BALANCE

ACCOUNTS RECEIVABLE LEDGER

Date	Explanation	P.R.	DEBIT	CREDIT	BALANCE

Date	Explanation	P.R.	DEBIT	CREDIT	BALANCE

Date	Explanation	P.R.	DEBIT	CREDIT	BALANCE

ACCOUNTS PAYABLE LEDGER

Date	Explanation	P.R.	DEBIT	CREDIT	BALANCE

Date	Explanation	P.R.	DEBIT	CREDIT	BALANCE

Date	Explanation	P.R.	DEBIT	CREDIT	BALANCE

Date	Explanation	P.R.	DEBIT	CREDIT	BALANCE

Trial Balance

Schedule of Accounts Receivable

Schedule of Accounts Payable

Sales Journal — Page 2

Date	Account Debited	Invoice Number	PR	Accts. Rec. Dr. Sales Cr.	Cost of Goods Sold Dr. Inventory Cr.

Cash Receipts Journal — Page 2

Date	Account Credited	Explanation	PR	Cash Dr.	Sales Disc. Dr.	Accts. Rec. Cr.	Serv. Rev. Cr.	Other Accts. Cr.	Cost of Goods Sold Dr. Inv. Cr.

Purchases Journal — Page 2

Date	Account	Date of Invo.	Terms	PR	Accts. Pay. Cr.	Inventory Dr.	Computer Supplies Dr.	Other Accts. Dr.

Name _____

					Cash Disbursements Journal				Page 2
Date	Ck. No.	Payee	Account Debited	PR	Cash Cr.	Inventory Cr.	Other Accts. Dr.	Accts. Payable Dr.

GENERAL JOURNAL				Page 2
Date	Account Titles and Explanation	P. R.	Debit	Credit

Sales Journal — Page 2

Date	Account Debited	Invoice Number	PR	Accts. Rec. Dr. Sales Cr.	Cost of Goods Sold Dr. Inventory Cr.

Cash Receipts Journal — Page 2

Date	Account Credited	Explanation	PR	Cash Dr.	Sales Disc. Dr.	Accts. Rec. Cr.	Sales Cr.	Other Accts. Cr.	Cost of Goods Sold Dr. Inv. Cr.

Purchases Journal — Page 2

Date	Account	Date of Invo.	Terms	PR	Accts. Pay. Cr.	Inventory Dr.	Office Supplies Dr.	Other Accts. Dr.

			Cash Disbursements Journal					Page 2	
Date	Ck. No.	Payee	Account Debited	PR	Cash Cr.	Inventory Cr.	Other Accts. Dr.	Accts. Payable Dr.

GENERAL JOURNAL   Page 2

Date	Account Titles and Explanation	P. R.	Debit	Credit
	Adjusting Entries			

	GENERAL JOURNAL			Page 2

Date			Account Titles and Explanation	P. R.	Debit	Credit
			Closing Entries			

GENERAL LEDGER

Cash   ACCOUNT NO. 101

Date	Explanation	P.R.	DEBIT	CREDIT	BALANCE
Apr. 30	Balance	√			50,247

Accounts Receivable   ACCOUNT NO. 106

Date	Explanation	P.R.	DEBIT	CREDIT	BALANCE
Apr. 30	Balance	√			4,725

Merchandise Inventory   ACCOUNT NO. 119

Date	Explanation	P.R.	DEBIT	CREDIT	BALANCE
Apr. 30	Balance	√			220,080

Office Supplies   ACCOUNT NO. 124

Date	Explanation	P.R.	DEBIT	CREDIT	BALANCE
Apr. 30	Balance	√			430

Store Supplies — ACCOUNT NO. 125

Date	Explanation	P.R.	DEBIT	CREDIT	BALANCE
Apr. 30	Balance	√			2,447

Prepaid Insurance — ACCOUNT NO. 128

Date	Explanation	P.R.	DEBIT	CREDIT	BALANCE
Apr. 30	Balance	√			3,318

Office Equipment — ACCOUNT NO. 163

Date	Explanation	P.R.	DEBIT	CREDIT	BALANCE
Apr. 30	Balance	√			22,470

Accumulated Depreciation-Office Equipment — ACCOUNT NO. 164

Date	Explanation	P.R.	DEBIT	CREDIT	BALANCE
Apr. 30	Balance	√			9,898

Store Equipment — ACCOUNT NO. 165

Date	Explanation	P.R.	DEBIT	CREDIT	BALANCE
Apr. 30	Balance	√			38,920

Accumulated Depreciation-Store Equipment — ACCOUNT NO. 166

Date	Explanation	P.R.	DEBIT	CREDIT	BALANCE
Apr. 30	Balance	√			17,556

Accounts Payable   ACCOUNT NO. 201

Date	Explanation	P.R.	DEBIT	CREDIT	BALANCE
Apr. 30	Balance	√			7,098

Paloma Chavez, Capital   ACCOUNT NO. 301

Date	Explanation	P.R.	DEBIT	CREDIT	BALANCE
Apr. 30	Balance	√			308,085

Paloma Chavez, Withdrawals   ACCOUNT NO. 302

Date	Explanation	P.R.	DEBIT	CREDIT	BALANCE

Sales   ACCOUNT NO. 413

Date	Explanation	P.R.	DEBIT	CREDIT	BALANCE

Sales Returns and Allowances   ACCOUNT NO. 414

Date	Explanation	P.R.	DEBIT	CREDIT	BALANCE

Sales Discounts   ACCOUNT NO. 415

Date	Explanation	P.R.	DEBIT	CREDIT	BALANCE

Cost of Goods Sold   ACCOUNT NO. 502

Date	Explanation	P.R.	DEBIT	CREDIT	BALANCE

Depreciation Expense-Office Equipment   ACCOUNT NO. 612

Date	Explanation	P.R.	DEBIT	CREDIT	BALANCE

Depreciation Expense-Store Equipment   ACCOUNT NO. 613

Date	Explanation	P.R.	DEBIT	CREDIT	BALANCE

Office Salaries Expense   ACCOUNT NO. 620

Date	Explanation	P.R.	DEBIT	CREDIT	BALANCE

Sales Salaries Expense   ACCOUNT NO. 621

Date	Explanation	P.R.	DEBIT	CREDIT	BALANCE

Insurance Expense — ACCOUNT NO. 637

Date	Explanation	P.R.	DEBIT	CREDIT	BALANCE

Rent Expense-Office Space — ACCOUNT NO. 641

Date	Explanation	P.R.	DEBIT	CREDIT	BALANCE

Rent Expense-Selling Space — ACCOUNT NO. 642

Date	Explanation	P.R.	DEBIT	CREDIT	BALANCE

Office Supplies Expense — ACCOUNT NO. 650

Date	Explanation	P.R.	DEBIT	CREDIT	BALANCE

Store Supplies Expense — ACCOUNT NO. 651

Date	Explanation	P.R.	DEBIT	CREDIT	BALANCE

Utilities Expense — ACCOUNT NO. 690

Date	Explanation	P.R.	DEBIT	CREDIT	BALANCE

	Income Summary				ACCOUNT NO. 901
Date	**Explanation**	**P.R.**	**DEBIT**	**CREDIT**	**BALANCE**

ACCOUNTS RECEIVABLE LEDGER

NAME   Bowman Company

Date	**Explanation**	**P.R.**	**DEBIT**	**CREDIT**	**BALANCE**

NAME   Dexter Corp.

Date	**Explanation**	**P.R.**	**DEBIT**	**CREDIT**	**BALANCE**

NAME   Karim Services

Date	**Explanation**	**P.R.**	**DEBIT**	**CREDIT**	**BALANCE**

NAME   Net, Inc.

Date	**Explanation**	**P.R.**	**DEBIT**	**CREDIT**	**BALANCE**
Apr. 30					4,725

ACCOUNTS PAYABLE LEDGER

NAME   Gates Supply Co.

Date	Explanation	P.R.	DEBIT	CREDIT	BALANCE

NAME   Gatsby Inc.

Date	Explanation	P.R.	DEBIT	CREDIT	BALANCE

NAME   Joey Corp.

Date	Explanation	P.R.	DEBIT	CREDIT	BALANCE

NAME   Parker Products

Date	Explanation	P.R.	DEBIT	CREDIT	BALANCE
Apr. 30					7,098

Name _____

Paloma Company
Work Sheet
For Month Ended May 31, 2008

Account Titles	Unadjusted Trial Balance		Adjustments		Adjusted Trial Balance		Income Statement		Balance Sheet & Statement of Owner's Equity	
	Dr.	Cr.	Dr.	Cr.	Dr.	Cr.	Dr.	Cr.	Dr.	Cr.

| Paloma Company |
| Income Statement |
| For Month Ended May 31, 2008 |

Paloma Company
Statement of Owner's Equity
For Month Ended May 31, 2008

Paloma Company
Balance Sheet
May 31, 2008

Paloma Company
Post-Closing Trial Balance
May 31, 2008

Paloma Company
Schedule of Accounts Receivable
May 31, 2008

Paloma Company
Schedule of Accounts Payable
May 31, 2008

(1) _____

_____

(2) _____

_____

_____

_____

_____

_____

_____

_____

_____

_____

_____

_____

_____

_____

_____

_____

(3) Fast Forward: _____

_____

_____

_____

_____

_____

_____

_____

Part 1

Best Buy's Return on Segment Assets

    Current Year--Domestic: _____

_____

    Current Year--International: _____

_____

    Prior Year--Domestic: _____

_____

    Prior Year--International: _____

_____

Circuit City's Return on Current Assets

    Current Year--Domestic: _____

_____

    Current Year--International: _____

_____

    Prior Year--Domestic: _____

_____

    Prior Year--International: _____

_____

Part 2--Analysis and Interpretation: _____

_____

_____

_____

_____

_____

_____

(1)

(2)

(3)

MEMORANDUM

TO:
FROM:
SUBJECT:
DATE:

(1)

(2)

(3)

(4)

				SALES JOURNAL	Page 2
Date	Account Debited	Invoice Number	PR	Accts. Rec. Dr. Sales Cr.	Cost of Goods Sold Dr. Inventory Cr.

					Cash Receipts Journal				Page 2
Date	Account Credited	Explanation	PR	Cash Dr.	Sales Disc. Dr.	Accts. Rec. Cr.	Sales Cr.	Other Accts. Cr.	Cost of Goods Sold Dr. Inv. Cr.

					Accts. Payable Cr.	Inventory Dr.	Office Supplies Dr.	Other Accts. Dr.
Date	**Account**	**Date of Invoice**	**Terms**	**PR**				

Purchases Journal — Page 2

						Cash Cr.	Inventory Cr.	Other Accts. Dr.	Accts. Payable Dr.
Date	**Ck. No.**	**Payee**	**Account Debited**	**PR**					

Cash Disbursements Journal — Page 2

GENERAL JOURNAL   Page 2

Date	Account Titles and Explanation	P.R.	Debit	Credit

GENERAL LEDGER

Cash   ACCOUNT NO. 101

Date	Explanation	P.R.	DEBIT	CREDIT	BALANCE

Accounts Receivable   ACCOUNT NO. 106

Date	Explanation	P.R.	DEBIT	CREDIT	BALANCE

Inventory   ACCOUNT NO. 119

Date	Explanation	P.R.	DEBIT	CREDIT	BALANCE

Office Supplies   ACCOUNT NO. 124

Date	Explanation	P.R.	DEBIT	CREDIT	BALANCE

Store Supplies   ACCOUNT NO. 125

Date	Explanation	P.R.	DEBIT	CREDIT	BALANCE

Office Equipment   ACCOUNT NO. 163

Date	Explanation	P.R.	DEBIT	CREDIT	BALANCE

Accounts Payable   ACCOUNT NO. 201

Date	Explanation	P.R.	DEBIT	CREDIT	BALANCE

Long-Term Notes Payable   ACCOUNT NO. 251

Date	Explanation	P.R.	DEBIT	CREDIT	BALANCE

_____, Capital   ACCOUNT NO. 301

Date	Explanation	P.R.	DEBIT	CREDIT	BALANCE

Sales   ACCOUNT NO. 413

Date	Explanation	P.R.	DEBIT	CREDIT	BALANCE

Sales Discounts   ACCOUNT NO. 415

Date	Explanation	P.R.	DEBIT	CREDIT	BALANCE

Cost of Goods Sold   ACCOUNT NO. 502

Date	Explanation	P.R.	DEBIT	CREDIT	BALANCE

Sales Salaries Expense   ACCOUNT NO. 621

Date	Explanation	P.R.	DEBIT	CREDIT	BALANCE

ACCOUNTS RECEIVABLE LEDGER

Date	Explanation	P.R.	DEBIT	CREDIT	BALANCE

Date	Explanation	P.R.	DEBIT	CREDIT	BALANCE

Date	Explanation	P.R.	DEBIT	CREDIT	BALANCE

ACCOUNTS PAYABLE LEDGER

Date	Explanation	P.R.	DEBIT	CREDIT	BALANCE

Date	Explanation	P.R.	DEBIT	CREDIT	BALANCE

Date	Explanation	P.R.	DEBIT	CREDIT	BALANCE

Date	Explanation	P.R.	DEBIT	CREDIT	BALANCE

Trial Balance

Schedule of Accounts Receivable

Schedule of Accounts Payable

(1) _____
_____
_____
_____

(2) _____
_____
_____
_____
_____
_____
_____

(3) _____
_____
_____
_____
_____
_____

(1) _____

_____

_____

_____

_____

_____

_____

_____

_____

_____

_____

_____

(2) _____

_____

_____

_____

_____

_____

_____

_____

_____

_____

_____

_____

_____

(1) _____
_____
_____
_____

(2) _____
_____
_____
_____

(3) _____
_____
_____
_____

(1) _____

_____

_____

_____

_____

_____

(2) _____

_____

_____

_____

_____

(3) _____

_____

_____

_____

_____

Quick Study 8-2
(1) _____

_____

_____

_____

_____

(2) _____

_____

_____

_____

Quick Study 8-3
(1) _____

_____

_____

(2) _____

_____

_____

(3) _____

_____

_____

(1) (a) _____

(b) _____

(c) _____

(2) _____

Quick Study 8-5
(1)

GENERAL JOURNAL

Date	Account Titles and Explanation	P. R.	Debit	Credit
(a) Establishment of the Fund:				
(b) Reimbursement of the Fund at Period-End:				

(2) _____
_____
_____
_____

Parts 1 and 2

	(1)		(2)
	Bank or Book Effect	**Add or Subtract**	**Journal Entry Required or Not**
(a)			
(b)			
(c)			
(d)			
(e)			
(f)			
(g)			

Quick Study 8-7

Days' Sales Uncollected (2008):

_____

_____

_____

_____

Days' Sales Uncollected (2007):

_____

_____

_____

_____

Interpretation and Explanation:

_____

_____

_____

_____

Quick Study 8-8[A]

_____

_____

_____

_____

_____

Quick Study 8-9[B]

(a) _____

_____

(b) _____

_____

_____

Evaluation:

_____

_____

_____

Principles Ignored:

_____

_____

_____

_____

_____

Exercise 8-2

(a) Internal Control Problems:

_____

_____

_____

_____

_____

_____

_____

_____

(b) Internal Control Recommendations:

_____

_____

_____

_____

_____

_____

Exercise 8-3

(1) _____

_____

_____

_____

_____

_____

(2) _____

_____

_____

_____

_____

_____

Name _____

(1) Establish the Fund

GENERAL JOURNAL

Date	Account Titles and Explanation	P. R.	Debit	Credit

(2) Reimburse the Fund

GENERAL JOURNAL

Date	Account Titles and Explanation	P. R.	Debit	Credit

(3) Reimburse and Increase the Fund

GENERAL JOURNAL

Date	Account Titles and Explanation	P. R.	Debit	Credit

(1) Establish the Fund

GENERAL JOURNAL

Date	Account Titles and Explanation	P. R.	Debit	Credit

(2) Reimburse the Fund

GENERAL JOURNAL

Date	Account Titles and Explanation	P.R.	Debit	Credit

(3) Adjust the Fund Balance

GENERAL JOURNAL

Date	Account Titles and Explanation	P. R.	Debit	Credit

		Bank Balance		Book Balance			Not Shown on the Reconciliation
		Add	Deduct	Add	Deduct	Adjust	
1.	NSF check from customer returned on Sept. 25 but not recorded by this company.						
2.	Interest earned on the account.						
3.	Deposit made on September 5 and processed by bank on September 6.						
4.	Check written by another depositor but charged against this company's account.						
5.	Bank service charge.						
6.	Checks outstanding on August 31 that cleared the bank in September.						
7.	Check written against the company account and cleared by the bank; erroneously not recorded by the company						
8.	Principal and interest on a note receivable to this company is collected by the bank but not yet recorded by the company.						
9.	Checks written and mailed to payees on October 2.						
10.	Checks written by the company and mailed to payees on September 30.						
11.	Deposit made on September 30 after the bank closed.						
12.	Special bank charge for collection of note in No. 8 on company's behalf.						

(1) _____

_____

_____

(2) _____

_____

(3) _____

_____

Exercise 8-8

_____

Bank Reconciliation

_____

_____

_____

_____

_____

_____

_____

_____

_____

_____

_____

Exercise 8-9

GENERAL JOURNAL

Date	Account Titles and Explanation	P. R.	Debit	Credit

Name _____

(a)

Days' Sales Uncollected (2007):

Days' Sales Uncollected (2008):

(b) Interpretation of Change:

Exercise 8-11^A

(1)		(3)		(5)	
(2)		(4)		(6)	

(a) Recording Invoices at Gross Amounts--Gross Method

GENERAL JOURNAL

Date	Account Titles and Explanation	P. R.	Debit	Credit

(b) Recording Invoices at Net Amounts--Net Method

GENERAL JOURNAL

Date	Account Titles and Explanation	P. R.	Debit	Credit

(1) **Principle Violated:**

   Recommended

(2) **Principle Violated:**

   Recommended

(3) **Principle Violated:**

   Recommended

(4) **Principle Violated:**

   Recommended

(5) **Principle Violated:**

   Recommended

Part 1

GENERAL JOURNAL

Date	Account Titles and Explanation	P. R.	Debit	Credit

Part 2

Petty Cash Payments Report

Part 3

GENERAL JOURNAL

Date	Account Titles and Explanation	P. R.	Debit	Credit

GENERAL JOURNAL

Date	Account Titles and Explanation	P. R.	Debit	Credit

Part 2

_____
_____
_____
_____
_____
_____
_____
_____
_____
_____

Part 1

Bank Reconciliation

Part 2

GENERAL JOURNAL

Date	Account Titles and Explanation	P. R.	Debit	Credit

(a)

(b)

Problem 8-5A or 8-5B
Part 1

Bank Reconciliation

GENERAL JOURNAL

Date	Account Titles and Explanation	P. R.	Debit	Credit

Part 3

(1) _____

_____

(2) _____

_____

(3) _____

_____

Bank Reconciliation

Part 2

GENERAL JOURNAL

Date	Account Titles and Explanation	P. R.	Debit	Credit

Part 1

	Feb. 26, 2005		Feb. 28, 2004	
Account	Balance ($)	Cash & Equiv. as % of Balance	Balance ($)	Cash & Equiv. as % of Balance

Interpretation: _____

_____

_____

Part 2

_____

_____

_____

_____

_____

_____

_____

_____

_____

_____

_____

_____

Days' Sales Uncollected (Feb. 26, 2005):

_____
_____
_____
_____
_____

Days' Sales Uncollected (Feb. 28, 2004):

_____
_____
_____
_____
_____

Interpretation:

_____
_____
_____
_____
_____

Part 4

Fast Forward:

_____
_____
_____
_____
_____
_____
_____
_____
_____

Best Buy:
Days' Sales Uncollected (Current year): _____
_____
_____
_____

Days' Sales Uncollected (Prior year): _____
_____
_____
_____

Interpretation: _____
_____
_____
_____
_____

Circuit City:
Days' Sales Uncollected (Current year): _____
_____
_____
_____

Days' Sales Uncollected (Prior year): _____
_____
_____
_____

Interpretation: _____
_____
_____
_____

Comparison - Best Buy vs. Circuit City: _____
_____
_____
_____
_____

(1) _____

_____

_____

_____

_____

(2) _____

_____

_____

_____

_____

(3) _____

_____

_____

_____

_____

_____

_____

(4) _____

_____

_____

_____

_____

_____

_____

MEMORANDUM

TO:
FROM:
SUBJECT:
DATE:

(1) _____
_____

(2) _____
_____

(3) _____
_____

(4) _____
_____

(5) _____
_____

(6) _____
_____

(7) _____
_____

(8) _____
_____

(9) _____
_____

(10) _____
_____
_____

(1) _____

(2) _____

(3) _____

(4) _____

(5) _____

(6) _____

(7) _____

(8) _____

(9) _____

(10) _____

(11) _____

_____

(1) _____

_____

_____

_____

(2) _____

_____

_____

_____

(3) _____

_____

_____

_____

(4) _____

_____

_____

_____

_____

(1) (a) _____

_____

_____

_____

(b) _____

_____

_____

(c) _____

_____

_____

(d) _____

_____

_____

(e) _____

_____

_____

(f) _____

_____

_____

(g) _____

_____

_____

(2) _____

_____

_____

Hitting the Road--BTN 8-9

_____

_____

_____

_____

_____

_____

_____

_____

_____

1.

Accounts	Current Year Balance	Cash as % of:	Prior Year Balance	Cash as % of Balance
Cash..........................				
Current Assets...........				
Current Liabilities.......				
Stockholders' equity...				
Total Assets...............				

Anaylsis Comment: _____

_____

_____

2. _____

_____

_____

_____

_____

3.

Days' Sales Uncollected

Current Year: _____

_____

_____

Prior Year: _____

_____

_____

Assessment: _____

_____

_____

_____

(1)

GENERAL JOURNAL

Date		Account Titles and Explanation	P. R.	Debit	Credit

(2)

GENERAL JOURNAL

Date		Account Titles and Explanation	P. R.	Debit	Credit

(1)

GENERAL JOURNAL

Date	Account Titles and Explanation	P. R.	Debit	Credit

(2)

GENERAL JOURNAL

Date	Account Titles and Explanation	P. R.	Debit	Credit

(1)

GENERAL JOURNAL

Date		Account Titles and Explanation	P. R.	Debit	Credit

(2) _____

_____

_____

Quick Study 9-4

GENERAL JOURNAL

Date		Account Titles and Explanation	P. R.	Debit	Credit

Quick Study 9-5

GENERAL JOURNAL

Date		Account Titles and Explanation	P. R.	Debit	Credit

GENERAL JOURNAL

Date	Account Titles and Explanation	P. R.	Debit	Credit

Quick Study 9-7

Accounts Receivable Turnover: _____

_____

_____

_____

Interpretation: _____

_____

_____

_____

GENERAL JOURNAL

Date	Account Titles and Explanation	P. R.	Debit	Credit

GENERAL LEDGER

Accounts Receivable	Sales	Sales Returns and Allowances

ACCOUNTS RECEIVABLE LEDGER

Ski Shop	Welcome Enterprises	Zia Natara

Part 2 _____

Schedule of Accounts Receivable

__Comparison:__

Name _____

GENERAL JOURNAL

Date	Account Titles and Explanation	P. R.	Debit	Credit

(a)

GENERAL JOURNAL

Date	Account Titles and Explanation	P. R.	Debit	Credit

(b)

GENERAL JOURNAL

Date	Account Titles and Explanation	P. R.	Debit	Credit

GENERAL JOURNAL

Date	Account Titles and Explanation	P. R.	Debit	Credit

Financial Statement Note(s): _____

_____

_____

_____

GENERAL JOURNAL

Date	Account Titles and Explanation	P. R.	Debit	Credit

GENERAL JOURNAL

Date	Account Titles and Explanation	P. R.	Debit	Credit

GENERAL JOURNAL

Date	Account Titles and Explanation	P. R.	Debit	Credit

Accounts Receivable Turnover (2007):

_____

_____

_____

Accounts Receivable Turnover (2008):

_____

_____

_____

Comparison and Interpretation:

_____

_____

_____

_____

GENERAL JOURNAL

Date	Account Titles and Explanation	P. R.	Debit	Credit

2007

GENERAL JOURNAL

Date		Account Titles and Explanation	P. R.	Debit	Credit

Supporting work:

2008

GENERAL JOURNAL

Date	Account Titles and Explanation	P. R.	Debit	Credit

Supporting work:

GENERAL JOURNAL

Date	Account Titles and Explanation	P. R.	Debit	Credit
(a)				
(b)				
(c)				

Part 2

_____
_____
_____
_____
_____
_____
_____
_____
_____

_____
_____
_____
_____
_____
_____

Problem 9-4A or 9-4B
Part 1

_____
_____
_____
_____
_____
_____
_____
_____
_____
_____

Part 2

GENERAL JOURNAL

Date	Account Titles and Explanation	P. R.	Debit	Credit

Part 3

_____
_____
_____
_____
_____
_____
_____
_____
_____
_____

Date	Account Titles and Explanation	P. R.	Debit	Credit
2007				
2008				

Date	Account Titles and Explanation	P. R.	Debit	Credit

Part 2

Reporting: _____
_____
_____
_____

Reasoning: _____
_____
_____
_____

Principle: _____
_____
_____
_____

GENERAL JOURNAL

Date	Account Titles and Explanation	P. R.	Debit	Credit
(a)				
(b)				

Part 2

_____

_____

_____

_____

_____

GENERAL JOURNAL

Date	Account Titles and Explanation	P. R.	Debit	Credit

Part 3

_____

_____

_____

_____

_____

_____

_____

(1) _____
_____
_____

(2) Accounts Receivable Turnover (2004): _____
_____
_____

(3) Average Collection Period: _____
_____

Analysis: _____
_____
_____

(4) Liquid Assets as a percent of Current Liabilities (Feb. 26, 2005): _____
_____
_____
_____

Liquid Assets as a percent of Current Liabilities (Feb. 28, 2004): _____
_____
_____
_____

Comparison and Interpretation: _____
_____
_____
_____
_____

(5) _____
_____
_____
_____

(6) Fast Forward: _____
_____
_____
_____
_____
_____
_____

(1) Best Buy's Accounts Receivable Turnover (Current Year and Prior Year):

_____
_____
_____
_____
_____

Circuit City's Accounts Receivable Turnover (Current Year and Prior Year):

_____
_____
_____
_____
_____

(2) Best Buy's Average Collection Period (Current Year and Prior Year):

_____
_____
_____
_____
_____

Circuit City's Average Collection Period (Current Year and Prior Year):

_____
_____
_____
_____
_____

(3) Efficiency Comparison:

_____
_____
_____
_____
_____

(1) _____

_____

_____

_____

_____

_____

_____

(2) _____

_____

_____

_____

_____

_____

_____

_____

(3) _____

_____

_____

_____

_____

_____

_____

Name _____

MEMORANDUM

TO:

FROM:

SUBJECT:

DATE:

(1) _____

_____

_____

_____

_____

_____

_____

(2) _____ Dec. 31, 2004 _____ Dec. 31, 2003

_____

_____

_____

_____

_____

_____

(3) _____

_____

_____

_____

Estimate of Uncollectibles: _____

_____

_____

_____

_____

_____

_____

Adjusting Entry:

GENERAL JOURNAL

Date	Account Titles and Explanation	P. R.	Debit	Credit

Presentation of Net Realizable Accounts Receivable in Balance Sheet:

_____

_____

_____

_____

_____

_____

(1) _____
_____
_____
_____

(2) _____
_____
_____
_____
_____
_____
_____

Added Monthly Net Income (Loss) under Plan A

_____

_____

_____

_____

_____

_____

_____

_____

Added Monthly Net Income (Loss) under Plan B

_____

_____

_____

_____

_____

_____

_____

_____

_____

Part 2

_____

_____

_____

_____

_____

_____

_____

_____

_____

_____

_____

_____

_____

_____

_____

_____

_____

_____

_____

_____

_____

_____

_____

_____

_____

_____

_____

_____

_____

_____

_____

_____

_____

_____

Global Decision--BTN 9-10

(1) _____

_____

_____

_____

_____

_____

_____

_____

(2) _____

_____

_____

_____

_____

_____

_____

_____
_____
_____
_____
_____
_____
_____

Quick Study 10-2

(1) _____
_____
_____

(2) _____
_____
_____

(3) _____
_____
_____

Quick Study 10-3

(1) Straight-line: _____
_____

(2) Units-of-Production: _____
_____
_____

Quick Study 10-4

Revised Straight-Line Depreciation: _____
_____
_____
_____
_____

First Year: _____
_____
_____

Second Year: _____
_____
_____

Third Year: _____
_____
_____

Quick Study 10-6

(1)

    (a) _____
    (b) _____
    (c) _____
    (d) _____

(2)

GENERAL JOURNAL

Date	Account Titles and Explanation	P. R.	Debit	Credit
(a)				
(d)				

GENERAL JOURNAL

Date	Account Titles and Explanation	P. R.	Debit	Credit
(1)				
(2)				
(3)				

Quick Study 10-8

GENERAL JOURNAL

Date	Account Titles and Explanation	P. R.	Debit	Credit
(1)				
(2)				

Intangible Asset(s): _____

_____

Natural Resource(s): _____

_____

Quick Study 10-10

GENERAL JOURNAL

Date		Account Titles and Explanation	P. R.	Debit	Credit
(1)					
(2)					

Quick Study 10-11

Total Asset Turnover: _____

_____

_____

Interpretation: _____

_____

_____

Name _____

GENERAL JOURNAL

Date	Account Titles and Explanation	P. R.	Debit	Credit
(1)				
(2)				

Exercise 10-1

Total Cost to be Recorded: _____

_____

_____

_____

_____

_____

_____

_____

Cost of Assets:

_____
_____
_____
_____
_____
_____
_____
_____

GENERAL JOURNAL

Date	Account Titles and Explanation	P. R.	Debit	Credit

Exercise 10-3
Allocation of Costs to Assets:

_____
_____
_____
_____
_____
_____
_____
_____
_____

GENERAL JOURNAL

Date	Account Titles and Explanation	P. R.	Debit	Credit

Name _____

(1) Straight-Line Depreciation:

Year	Annual Depreciation	Year-End Book Value

(2) Double-Declining-Balance Depreciation:

Year	Beginning-Year Book Value	Depreciation Rate	Annual Depreciation	Year-End Book Value

(1) Straight-Line:

_____

_____

_____

_____

(2) Units-of-Production:

_____

_____

_____

_____

_____

(3) Double-Declining-Balance:

_____

_____

_____

_____

_____

_____

Exercise 10-6

(1) Straight-Line:

_____

_____

_____

(2) Double-Declining-Balance:

_____

_____

_____

_____

_____

_____

_____

(1) _____
_____
_____
_____
_____

(2) _____
_____
_____
_____
_____
_____
_____
_____

(1) Straight-Line Depreciation:

Year	Income before Depreciation	Depreciation Expense	Net Income

(2) Double-Declining-Balance Depreciation:

Year	Income before Depreciation	Depreciation Expense	Net Income

(1) _____

_____

_____

_____

_____

(2)

GENERAL JOURNAL

Date	Account Titles and Explanation	P. R.	Debit	Credit

(3) _____

_____

_____

_____

_____

_____

(4)

GENERAL JOURNAL

Date	Account Titles and Explanation	P. R.	Debit	Credit

GENERAL JOURNAL

Date	Account Titles and Explanation	P. R.	Debit	Credit
(1)				
(2)				
(3)				

Exercise 10-11

GENERAL JOURNAL

Date	Account Titles and Explanation	P. R.	Debit	Credit
(1)				
(2)				
(3)				
(4)				

GENERAL JOURNAL

Date		Account Titles and Explanation	P. R.	Debit	Credit
(1)					
(2)					

Computations:

Exercise 10-13

GENERAL JOURNAL

Date		Account Titles and Explanation	P. R.	Debit	Credit

GENERAL JOURNAL

Date	Account Titles and Explanation	P. R.	Debit	Credit

Exercise 10-15

(1) Value of Goodwill: _____

_____

_____

(2) _____

_____

(3) _____

_____

_____

Exercise 10-16

(1) _____

(2) _____

(3) _____

_____

Name _____

Total Asset Turnover (2007): _____

_____

_____

Total Asset Turnover (2008): _____

_____

_____

Efficiency Analysis: _____

_____

_____

_____

_____

Exercise 10-18^A

(1) _____

_____

_____

(2) _____

_____

_____

(3) _____

_____

_____

GENERAL JOURNAL

Date	Account Titles and Explanation	P. R.	Debit	Credit
(1)				
(2)				
(3)				

Part 1

	Estimated Market Value	Percent of Total	Apportioned Cost
Building.............................			
Land.................................			
Land Improvments..............			
Vehicles (or Trucks)............	_____		_____
Total................................	==========		=================

GENERAL JOURNAL

Date	Account Titles and Explanation	P. R.	Debit	Credit

Part 2

_____
_____
_____
_____

Part 3

_____
_____
_____
_____
_____
_____

Part 4

_____
_____
_____
_____
_____
_____
_____

Part 1

	Land	Building 2 (or B)	Building 3 (or C)	Land Improv. 1 (or B)	Land Improv. 2 (or C)
Purchase price.........					
Demolition..............					
Land grading...........					
New building...........					
New improvements...					
Totals....................					

Computations:

Part 2

GENERAL JOURNAL

Date	Account Titles and Explanation	P. R.	Debit	Credit

Part 3

GENERAL JOURNAL

Date	Account Titles and Explanation	P. R.	Debit	Credit

2007:

GENERAL JOURNAL

Date	Account Titles and Explanation	P. R.	Debit	Credit

Supporting work:

2008:

GENERAL JOURNAL

Date	Account Titles and Explanation	P. R.	Debit	Credit

Supporting work:

2007:

GENERAL JOURNAL

Date		Account Titles and Explanation	P. R.	Debit	Credit

2008:

GENERAL JOURNAL

Date		Account Titles and Explanation	P. R.	Debit	Credit

Supporting work:

GENERAL JOURNAL

Date	Account Titles and Explanation	P. R.	Debit	Credit

Supporting work:

Year	Straight-Line	Units-of-Production	Double-Declining-Balance
1			
2			
3			
4			
5 (for 10-5B)	_____	_____	_____
Totals	_____	_____	_____

Workspace:

Straight-Line:

_____

_____

Units-of-Production:

_____

_____

_____

_____

Double-Declining-Balance:

_____

_____

_____

_____

Problem 10-6A or 10-6B

Part 1

GENERAL JOURNAL

Date	Account Titles and Explanation	P. R.	Debit	Credit

(a) and (b)

GENERAL JOURNAL

Date		Account Titles and Explanation	P. R.	Debit	Credit

Part 3

GENERAL JOURNAL

Date		Account Titles and Explanation	P. R.	Debit	Credit
(a) Sold for $		**_____ cash:**			
(b) Sold for $		**_____ cash:**			
(c) Destroyed in fire, collected $_____ cash from insurance.					

GENERAL JOURNAL

Date	Account Titles and Explanation	P. R.	Debit	Credit
(a)				
(b)				
(c)				
(d)				

Analysis Component:

_____

_____

_____

_____

_____

_____

_____

_____

GENERAL JOURNAL

Date		Account Titles and Explanation	P. R.	Debit	Credit
(a)					
(b)					
(c)					

Part 2

GENERAL JOURNAL

Date		Account Titles and Explanation	P. R.	Debit	Credit
(a)					
(b)					
(c)					

(1) _____

_____

_____

_____

_____

_____

(2)	December 31, 2007	December 31, 2008
Office Equipment:		

_____

_____

_____

_____

_____

Computer Equipment: _____

_____

_____

_____

_____

_____

(3) Total Asset Turnover: _____

_____

_____

_____

_____

Analysis: _____

_____

_____

_____

_____

(1) As of Feb. 26, 2005:

_____

_____

_____

As of Feb. 28, 2004

_____

_____

_____

_____

(2)

_____

_____

_____

(3)

_____

_____

_____

_____

_____

(4) Total Asset Turnover (2005):

_____

_____

_____

Total Asset Turnover (2004):

_____

_____

_____

(5) Fast Forward:

_____

_____

_____

_____

(1) Total Asset Turnover (Best Buy): _____

     Current Year

_____

_____

     One Year Prior

_____

_____

   Total Asset Turnover (Circuit City): _____

     Current Year

_____

_____

     One Year Prior

_____

_____

(2) Efficiency Analysis: _____

_____

_____

_____

_____

(1) _____

_____

_____

_____

_____

_____

_____

_____

(2) _____

_____

_____

_____

_____

_____

_____

_____

_____

_____

(3) _____

_____

_____

_____

_____

_____

_____

_____

_____

_____

DATA FOR MEMORANDUM						
Total Asset Turnover	Company 1	Company 2	Company 3	Company 4	Company 5	Average

MEMORANDUM

TO:
FROM:
SUBJECT:
DATE:

Name _____

(1) _____

_____

_____

_____

_____

_____

(2)

	Amount	$ Change from Prior Year	% Change

(3) _____

_____

_____

_____

_____

_____

(4) _____

_____

_____

_____

_____

Presentation Outline

Method of Expertise: _____
_____
_____
_____
_____
_____

Depreciation Expense: _____
_____
_____
_____
_____
_____
_____

Explanations: _____
_____
_____
_____
_____
_____
_____

Analysis Versus Other Methods: _____
_____
_____
_____
_____
_____
_____

Book Value and Reporting: _____
_____
_____
_____
_____
_____

Name _____

(1) _____
_____
_____
_____
_____
_____
_____
_____

(2) _____
_____
_____
_____

(3) _____
_____
_____
_____
_____
_____

(a) _____

_____

_____

_____

_____

_____

_____

_____

(b) _____

_____

_____

_____

_____

_____

_____

Part 2

_____

_____

_____

_____

_____

_____

_____

_____

_____
_____
_____
_____
_____
_____
_____
_____
_____
_____
_____
_____
_____
_____
_____
_____
_____
_____
_____
_____
_____

Global Decision--BTN 10-10

(1) Total Asset Turnover (Current Year): _____
_____
_____

Total Asset Turnover (Prior Year): _____
_____
_____

(2) _____
_____
_____
_____
_____
_____

Current Liabilities: _____

_____

_____

Quick Study 11-2

GENERAL JOURNAL

Date	Account Titles and Explanation	P. R.	Debit	Credit

Quick Study 11-3

GENERAL JOURNAL

Date	Account Titles and Explanation	P. R.	Debit	Credit

(1) Accrued Interest Payable: _____

_____

_____

_____

(2) & (3)

GENERAL JOURNAL

Date	Account Titles and Explanation	P. R.	Debit	Credit

Quick Study 11-5

GENERAL JOURNAL

Date	Account Titles and Explanation	P. R.	Debit	Credit

Quick Study 11-6

GENERAL JOURNAL

Date	Account Titles and Explanation	P. R.	Debit	Credit

GENERAL JOURNAL

Date	Account Titles and Explanation	P. R.	Debit	Credit

Quick Study 11-8

GENERAL JOURNAL

Date	Account Titles and Explanation	P. R.	Debit	Credit

Quick Study 11-9

(1) _____

(2) _____

(3) _____

Quick Study 11-10

Times Interest Earned: _____

_____

_____

Interpretation: _____

_____

_____

Quick Study 11-11[B]

GENERAL JOURNAL

Date	Account Titles and Explanation	P. R.	Debit	Credit

(1) _____   (6) _____
(2) _____   (7) _____
(3) _____   (8) _____
(4) _____   (9) _____
(5) _____   (10) _____

Exercise 11-2

GENERAL JOURNAL

Date		Account Titles and Explanation	P. R.	Debit	Credit
(1)					
(2)					
(3)					
(4)					
(5)					
(6)					

1. _____

_____

_____

_____

2.

GENERAL JOURNAL

Date	Account Titles and Explanation	P. R.	Debit	Credit

3.

GENERAL JOURNAL

Date	Account Titles and Explanation	P. R.	Debit	Credit

(1) Maturity Date: _____

_____

_____

(2)

GENERAL JOURNAL

Date	Account Titles and Explanation	P. R.	Debit	Credit

(1) Maturity Date: _____
_____
_____

(2) Interest Expense (2008): _____
_____
_____
_____

(3) Interest Expense (2009): _____
_____
_____
_____

(4)

GENERAL JOURNAL

Date	Account Titles and Explanation	P. R.	Debit	Credit

Name _____

	Subject to Tax	Rate	Tax
(a)			
FICA-Social Security..........	_____	_____	_____
FICA-Medicare..................	_____	_____	_____
FUTA...............................	_____	_____	_____
SUTA...............................	_____	_____	_____
(b)			
FICA-Social Security..........	_____	_____	_____
FICA-Medicare..................	_____	_____	_____
FUTA...............................	_____	_____	_____
SUTA...............................	_____	_____	_____
(c)			
FICA-Social Security..........	_____	_____	_____
FICA-Medicare..................	_____	_____	_____
FUTA...............................	_____	_____	_____
SUTA...............................	_____	_____	_____

GENERAL JOURNAL

Date	Account Titles and Explanation	P. R.	Debit	Credit

Exercise 11-8

(1) _____

_____

(2) _____

_____

(3) _____

_____

(4) _____

_____

_____

(5)

GENERAL JOURNAL

Date	Account Titles and Explanation	P. R.	Debit	Credit

Exercise 11-9

(a) _____
_____

(b) _____
_____

(c) _____
_____

(d) _____
_____

(e) _____
_____

(f) _____
_____

Analysis: _____
_____
_____

Chapter 11   Exercise 11-10^{A} Name _____

_____

_____

_____

_____

_____

_____

_____

_____

_____

_____

Exercise 11-11^{A}

_____

_____

_____

_____

_____

_____

_____

_____

_____

_____

_____

_____

Exercise 11-12^{B}

(1) _____

_____

_____

_____

_____

(2)

GENERAL JOURNAL

Date	Account Titles and Explanation	P. R.	Debit	Credit

(1) Maturity Dates: _____

_____

_____

_____

_____

_____

_____

(2) Interest Due at Maturity: _____

_____

_____

_____

_____

_____

_____

(3) Accrued Interest at the End of 2007: _____

_____

_____

_____

_____

_____

(4) Interest Expense in 2008: _____

_____

_____

_____

_____

_____

(5)

GENERAL JOURNAL

Date	Account Titles and Explanation	P. R.	Debit	Credit

(1)

GENERAL JOURNAL

Date	Account Titles and Explanation	P. R.	Debit	Credit
2007				

(1) (Continued from prior page)

GENERAL JOURNAL

Date	Account Titles and Explanation	P. R.	Debit	Credit
2008				

(2) Warranty Expense for November 2007 and December 2007:

_____
_____
_____
_____
_____
_____

(3) Warranty Expense for January 2008:

_____
_____
_____
_____
_____

(4) Balance of the Estimated Warranty Liability as of December 31, 2007:

_____
_____
_____
_____

(5) Balance of the Estimated Warranty Liability as of January 31, 2008:

_____
_____
_____
_____

(1) _____ Company:

Times Interest Earned: _____

_____

_____

_____

_____

(2) _____ Company:

Times Interest Earned: _____

_____

_____

_____

_____

(3) Sales Increase by _____ %

	_____ Company	_____ Company
Sales		
Variable expenses		
Income before interest		
Interest expense (fixed)		
Net Income		
Net income percent change		

(4) Sales Increase by _____ %

	_____ Company	_____ Company
Sales		
Variable expenses		
Income before interest		
Interest expense (fixed)		
Net Income		
Net income percent change		

(5)   Sales Increase by _____ %

	_____ Company	_____ Company
Sales		
Variable expenses		
Income before interest		
Interest expense (fixed)		
Net Income		
Net income percent change		

(6)   Sales Decrease by _____ %

	_____ Company	_____ Company
Sales		
Variable expenses		
Income before interest		
Interest expense (fixed)		
Net Income		
Net income percent change		

(7)   Sales Decrease by _____ %

	_____ Company	_____ Company
Sales		
Variable expenses		
Income before interest		
Interest expense (fixed)		
Net Income		
Net income percent change		

(8)   Sales Decrease by _____ %

	_____ Company	_____ Company
Sales		
Variable expenses		
Income before interest		
Interest expense (fixed)		
Net Income		
Net income percent change		

(9) Analysis: _____
_____
_____
_____
_____
_____
_____
_____
_____
_____

(1) Each Employee's FICA Withholdings for Social Security:

	__	__	__	__	Total
Maximum base					
Earned through _____					
Amt. subject to tax					
Earned this week					
Subject to tax					
Tax rate					
Social Security tax					

(2) Each Employee's FICA Withholdings for Medicare:

	__	__	__	__	Total
Earned this week					
Tax rate					
Medicare tax					

(3) Employer's FICA Taxes for Social Security:

	__	__	__	__	Total

(4) Employer's FICA Taxes for Medicare:

	__	__	__	__	Total

(5) Employer's FUTA Taxes:

	—	—	—	—	**Total**
Maximum base					
Earned through _____					
Amt. subject to tax					
Earned this week					
Subject to tax					
Tax rate					
FUTA rate					

(6) Employer's SUTA Taxes:

	—	—	—	—	**Total**
Subject to tax					
Tax rate					
SUTA tax					

(7) Each Employee's Net (Take-Home) Pay:

	—	—	—	—	**Total**
Gross earnings					
Less:					
FICA Soc. Sec. tax					
FICA Medicare tax					
Withholding taxes					
Health Insurance					
Take-home pay					

(8) Employer's Total Payroll-Related Expense for Each Employee:

	—	—	—	—	**Total**
Gross earnings					
Plus:					
FICA Soc. Sec. tax					
FICA Medicare tax					
FUTA tax					
SUTA tax					
Health Insurance					
Pension contrib.					
Total payroll exp.					

(1)

GENERAL JOURNAL

Date	Account Titles and Explanation	P. R.	Debit	Credit

(2)

GENERAL JOURNAL

Date	Account Titles and Explanation	P. R.	Debit	Credit

GENERAL JOURNAL

Date	Account Titles and Explanation	P. R.	Debit	Credit

Work Space:

GENERAL JOURNAL

Date	Account Titles and Explanation	P. R.	Debit	Credit
Continued from prior page				

Work Space:

(1) _____

_____

_____

_____

_____

_____

GENERAL JOURNAL

Date	Account Titles and Explanation	P. R.	Debit	Credit
(2)				
(3)				
(4)				

Work Space:

(a) Correct Ending Balance of Cash and the Amount of the Omitted Check:

_____
_____
_____
_____
_____
_____
_____
_____
_____
_____
_____

(b) Allowance for Doubtful Accounts:

_____
_____
_____
_____
_____
_____

(c) Depreciation Expense on the Truck:

_____
_____
_____
_____
_____
_____
_____

(d) Depreciation Expense on the Equipment:

_____
_____
_____
_____
_____

(e) Adjusted Revenue and Unearned Revenue Balances:

_____
_____
_____
_____
_____
_____
_____
_____
_____
_____
_____
_____
_____
_____
_____
_____

(f) Warranty Expense and Estimated Warranty Liability:

_____
_____
_____
_____
_____
_____
_____
_____
_____

(g) Interest Payable and Interest Expense:

_____
_____
_____
_____
_____
_____
_____
_____
_____
_____
_____
_____

BUG-OFF EXTERMINATORS
December 31, 2008

Account Titles	Unadjusted Trial Balance		Adjustments		Adjusted Trial Balance	
	Dr.	Cr.	Dr.	Cr.	Dr.	Cr.
Cash						
Accounts Receivable						
Allowance for Doubtful Accounts						
Merchandise Inventory						
Trucks						
Accumulated Depreciation-Trucks						
Equipment						
Accum. Depreciation-Equipment						
Accounts Payable						
Estimated Warranty Liability						
Unearned Services Revenue						
Interest Payable						
Long-Term Notes Payable						
D. Buggs, Capital						
D. Buggs, Withdrawals						
Extermination Services Revenue						
Interest Revenue						
Sales						
Cost of Goods Sold						
Depreciation Expense-Trucks						
Depreciation Expense-Equipment						
Wages Expense						
Interest Expense						
Rent Expense						
Bad Debts Expense						
Miscellaneous Expense						
Repairs Expense						
Utilities Expense						
Warranty Expense						
Totals						

GENERAL JOURNAL

Date		Account Titles and Explanation	P. R.	Debit	Credit

BUG-OFF EXTERMINATORS
Income Statement
For Year Ended December 31, 2008

BUG-OFF EXTERMINATORS
Statement of Owner's Equity
For Year Ended December 31, 2008

BUG-OFF EXTERMINATORS
Balance Sheet
December 31, 2008

Name _____

(1) Times Interest Earned (2005): _____

_____

_____

Times Interest Earned (2004): _____

_____

_____

Times Interest Earned (2003): _____

_____

_____

Interpretation: _____

_____

_____

_____

_____

(2) _____

_____

_____

_____

(3) _____

_____

_____

_____

(4) Fast Forward: _____

_____

_____

_____

_____

_____

(1) Best Buy's Times Interest Earned (Current Year):

_____

_____

    Best Buy's Times Interest Earned (One Year Prior):

_____

_____

    Best Buy's Times Interest Earned (Two Years Prior):

_____

_____

    Circuit City's Times Interest Earned (Current Year):

_____

_____

    Circuit City's Times Interest Earned (One Year Prior):

_____

_____

    Circuit City's Times Interest Earned (Two Years Prior):

_____

_____

(2)   Interpretation:

_____

_____

_____

_____

_____

(1) _____
_____
_____
_____
_____
_____
_____
_____
_____
_____

(2) _____
_____
_____
_____
_____
_____
_____
_____
_____
_____
_____
_____
_____
_____
_____

Name _____

MEMORANDUM

TO:
FROM:
SUBJECT:
DATE:

(1) _____
_____
_____
_____

(2) _____
_____
_____
_____

(3) _____
_____
_____
_____
_____
_____

Teamwork in Action--BTN 11-6

(1) _____
_____
_____
_____
_____
_____

(2)

GENERAL JOURNAL

Date	Account Titles and Explanation	P. R.	Debit	Credit

(3) Team Discussion

(4)

GENERAL JOURNAL

Date	Account Titles and Explanation	P. R.	Debit	Credit

(5) Team Discussion

Chapter 11   Business Week Activity   Name _____
            BTN 11-7

(1) _____
_____
_____
_____
_____

(2) _____
_____
_____
_____
_____
_____

| Income Statement (Prospective) | | |
California	Hawaii	Total
Sales		
Cost of Goods Sold (30%)		
Gross Profit		
Operating Expenses (25%)		
Income before interest		
Interest expense		
Net income		

Part 2

Times Interest Earned: _____

_____

_____

_____

Part 3

| Income Statement (Prospective) | | |
California	Hawaii	Total
Sales		
Cost of Goods Sold (30%)		
Gross Profit		
Operating Expenses (25%)		
Income before interest		
Interest expense		
Net Income		

Times Interest Earned: _____

_____

_____

| Income Statement (Prospective) | | | |
	California	Hawaii	Total
Sales			
Cost of Goods Sold (30%)			
Gross Profit			
Operating Expenses (25%)			
Income before interest			
Interest expense			
Net Income			

Times Interest Earned:

Part 5

_____
_____
_____
_____
_____
_____
_____
_____
_____
_____
_____
_____
_____
_____
_____
_____
_____
_____
_____
_____
_____

Global Decision--BTN 11-10

(1) Times Interest Earned	Current Year	One Year Prior

(2) _____
_____
_____
_____
_____
_____
_____

(a) _____

_____

_____

(b) _____

_____

_____

Quick Study 12-2

	Share to Stolton	Share to Bright	Total
Net income			
Salary allowance:			
Stolton			
Bright			
Total salary allowances			
Balance of income			
Balance allocated:			
Stolton			
Bright			
Total allocated			
Balance of income			
Shares of the partners			

Quick Study 12-3

_____

_____

_____

_____

_____

Quick Study 12-4

_____

_____

_____

_____

_____

GENERAL JOURNAL

Date	Account Titles and Explanation	P. R.	Debit	Credit

Quick Study 12-6

GENERAL JOURNAL

Date	Account Titles and Explanation	P. R.	Debit	Credit

Quick Study 12-7

_____
_____
_____
_____
_____
_____
_____
_____
_____
_____
_____

	Characteristic	General Partnerships
1.	Life	
2.	Owners' liability	
3.	Legal status	
4.	Tax status of income	
5.	Owners' authority	
6.	Ease of formation	
7.	Transferability of ownership	
8.	Ability to raise large amounts of capital	

Exercise 12-2
Part a

Recommended Organization: _____

_____

_____

_____

_____

Taxation Effects: _____

_____

_____

Advantages: _____

_____

_____

_____

Recommended Organization: _____
_____
_____
_____
_____
_____

Taxation Effects: _____
_____
_____
_____

Advantages: _____
_____
_____
_____

Part c

Recommended Organization: _____
_____
_____
_____
_____
_____

Taxation Effects: _____
_____
_____

Advantages: _____
_____
_____
_____

(1)

GENERAL JOURNAL

Date	Account Titles and Explanation	P. R.	Debit	Credit
(a)				
(b)				
(c)				

(2)

Capital account balances:	Eckert	Kelley
Initial investment		
Withdrawals		
Share of income		
Ending balances		

	Share to Kramer	Share to Knox	Total
(1)			
(2)			
(3)			

	Share to Kramer	Share to Knox	Total
(1)			

(2)

Exercise 12-6

GENERAL JOURNAL

Date	Account Titles and Explanation	P. R.	Debit	Credit

(1)

GENERAL JOURNAL

Date	Account Titles and Explanation	P. R.	Debit	Credit

(2)

GENERAL JOURNAL

Date	Account Titles and Explanation	P. R.	Debit	Credit

(3)

GENERAL JOURNAL

Date	Account Titles and Explanation	P. R.	Debit	Credit

(1)

GENERAL JOURNAL

Date	Account Titles and Explanation	P. R.	Debit	Credit

(2)

GENERAL JOURNAL

Date	Account Titles and Explanation	P. R.	Debit	Credit

(3)

GENERAL JOURNAL

Date	Account Titles and Explanation	P. R.	Debit	Credit

(1)

	Red	White	Blue	Total
Initial investments				
Allocation of all losses				
Capital balances				

(2)

GENERAL JOURNAL

Date	Account Titles and Explanation	P. R.	Debit	Credit

(3)

GENERAL JOURNAL

Date	Account Titles and Explanation	P. R.	Debit	Credit

(a) Loss computation from selling assets: _____

_____

_____

_____

_____

_____

_____

_____

_____

(b) Loss allocation

	Turner	Roth	Lowe	Total
Capital balance before loss liquidation......................				
Allocation of loss:				
Capital balances after loss............				

(c) Liability to be paid: _____

_____

_____

(a) Loss computation from selling assets:

_____
_____
_____
_____
_____
_____
_____

(b) Loss and deficit allocation:

	Turner	Roth	Lowe	Total
Capital balance before loss.........				
Allocation of loss:				
Capital balances after loss............				
Allocation of _____ deficit to				
Cash paid by each partner............				

(c) Liability to be paid:

_____

Exercise 12-12

_____
_____
_____
_____
_____
_____
_____
_____
_____

GENERAL JOURNAL

Date	Account Titles and Explanation	P. R.	Debit	Credit
(1)				
(2)				
(3)				

Supporting calculations:

_____
_____
_____
_____
_____
_____
_____
_____
_____
_____
_____
_____
_____
_____
_____
_____
_____

Inc./Loss Sharing Plan	Year 1 Calculations		
(a)			
(b)			
(c)			
(d)			

Inc./Loss Sharing Plan	Year 2 Calculations		
(a)			
(b)			
(c)			
(d)			

Inc./Loss Sharing Plan	Year 3		
	Calculations		
(a)			
(b)			
(c)			
(d)			

Supporting Work Space:

Inc./Loss Sharing Plan	Calculations			Total
(a)				
(b)				
(c)				

_____ PARTNERSHIP
Statement of Partners' Equity
For Year Ended December 31

				Total
Beg. capital balances				
Plus:				
Owner investments				
Net Income:				
Salary allowances				
Interest allowances				
Balance allocated				
Total net income				
Total				
Less partners' withdrawals				
End. capital balances				

Part 3

GENERAL JOURNAL

Date	Account Titles and Explanation	P. R.	Debit	Credit

GENERAL JOURNAL

Date		Account Titles and Explanation	P. R.	Debit	Credit
(a)					
(b)					
(c)					
(d)					
(e)					

Chapter 12 Problem 12-4A or 12-4B Name ______________________
Part 2 (Continued)

GENERAL JOURNAL

Date		Account Titles and Explanation	P. R.	Debit	Credit
(a)					
(b)					
(c)					

(1)

GENERAL JOURNAL

Date	Account Titles and Explanation	P. R.	Debit	Credit

(2)

GENERAL JOURNAL

Date	Account Titles and Explanation	P. R.	Debit	Credit

(3)

GENERAL JOURNAL

Date	Account Titles and Explanation	P. R.	Debit	Credit

(4)

GENERAL JOURNAL

Date	Account Titles and Explanation	P. R.	Debit	Credit

(1) _____

_____

_____

_____

_____

_____

_____

_____

_____

_____

_____

(2)   GENERAL JOURNAL

Date	Account Titles and Explanation	P. R.	Debit	Credit

(3)   GENERAL JOURNAL

Date	Account Titles and Explanation	P. R.	Debit	Credit

(4) _____

_____

_____

_____

_____

(1)
_____
_____
_____
_____
_____
_____
_____

(2)
_____
_____
_____
_____
_____
_____
_____
_____
_____

(3)
_____
_____
_____
_____
_____
_____
_____
_____

Comparative Analysis--BTN 12-2

(1)
_____
_____

(2)
_____
_____
_____

(3)
_____
_____

(4)
_____
_____
_____
_____

(1) Income allocation per original agreement:

	Maben	Orlando	Clark	Total
Salary allowance				
Per patient charges				
Totals				

(2) Income allocation per Clark's proposal:

	Maben	Orlando	Clark	Total
Per patient charges				

(3)

_____
_____
_____
_____
_____
_____
_____
_____
_____

STUDY NOTES
Organizations with Partnership Characteristics

_____
_____
_____
_____
_____
_____
_____
_____
_____
_____
_____
_____
_____
_____
_____
_____
_____
_____
_____
_____
_____
_____
_____
_____
_____
_____
_____
_____
_____
_____
_____
_____
_____
_____
_____
_____
_____
_____
_____
_____
_____
_____
_____
_____

(1) _____

_____

_____

_____

_____

_____

(2) _____

_____

_____

_____

_____

(3) _____

_____

_____

_____

_____

_____

(1)

Income/Loss Sharing Plan	Calculations	Baker	Warner	Rice	Total

(a) _____

_____

(b) _____

_____

_____

_____

_____

(c) _____

_____

_____

_____

_____

_____

_____

(d) _____

_____

_____

_____

_____

_____

_____

_____

_____

_____

(2) Team members share solutions.

(3) _____

_____

_____

_____

_____

_____

_____

_____

_____

(1) _____

_____

_____

_____

_____

(2) _____

_____

_____

_____

_____

(3) _____

_____

_____

_____

_____

Entrepreneurial Decision--BTN 12-8

(1) _____

_____

_____

_____

_____

_____

(2) _____

_____

_____

_____

(3) _____

_____

_____

_____

_____

(1) _____

_____

_____

_____

(2) _____

_____

_____

(3) _____

_____

_____

_____

_____

_____

_____

_____

_____

_____